Method of Moments
in Applied Mathematics

Russian Monographs and Texts on Advanced Mathematics and Physics

Additional Volumes in Preparation

Method of Moments in Applied Mathematics

by YU V. VOROBYEV

Translated from the Russian
by BERNARD SECKLER

GORDON AND BREACH SCIENCE PUBLISHERS
New York · London · Paris

Editorial offices for Great Britain and Europe:
Gordon and Breach, Science Publishers Ltd.
171 Strand, London W.C.2, England

Distributed in the United Kingdom by:
Blackie & Son Ltd.
5 Fitzhardinge Street, London W.1, England

Printed in Great Britain by Blackie & Son Ltd.
Bishopbriggs, Glasgow

Annotation

This book presents the theory behind the moment method of finding the eigenvalues of a linear operator approximately and of solving linear problems. The theory is illustrated by a number of specific applied problems. It is intended for research workers and post-graduates in the fields of applied mathematics, physics, and engineering, as well as for students in senior courses in corresponding specialties.

Preface

Numerous problems in mechanics, physics, and engineering lead to either non-homogeneous linear equations (as in statics problems) or homogeneous linear equations (as in oscillation problems). The idea of using the method of successive approximations (an iterative method) to solve such equations was conceived of long ago. Liouville [1] employed an iterative method in his work on linear differential equations. The same method was applied by Neumann in potential theory [1]. (Numbers in parentheses refer to the bibliography at the end of the book).

A number of difficulties are encountered in the solution of linear equations by successive approximations. First of all, the approximations may not converge to the solution. This greatly narrows down the class of problems to which the method may be applied. Second, even if the approximations did converge to the solution, it often happens that the convergence is much too slow and a formidable number of computations must be performed to obtain satisfactory accuracy.

The limited range of applicability of these methods and the slow convergence of the approximations for a time turned interest away from the theory of iterative methods. Only lately with the advent of high-speed automatic computing machines have iterative methods with their simple computational schemes begun to be widely used in practical applications. This of course has restimulated interest in their theory.

Thus, in recent years, a vast number of diverse iterative methods have been developed. This book will present but one class of methods based on a variational principle and closely related to the Chebyshev-Markov classical problem of moments. However, these methods are distinguished by the broad group of problems to which they may be applied and by the rapidity of convergence of the successive approximations.

A general formulation of the problem and the use of functional analysis has enabled all these methods to be consolidated into a single method of moments.

To facilitate reading the book, the author thought it essential to include at requisite points a brief but, as far as possible, understandable resumé of the terminology and basic results of linear operator theory in Hilbert space. However, for a better understanding of certain sections, it will be necessary to have a familiarity with the spectral theory of self-adjoint operators and the theory of unbounded operators. These topics are given excellent treatment in *Elements of Functional Analysis* by L. A. Lyusternik and S. L. Sobolev, and *Lectures on Functional Analysis* by F. Riesz and B. Sz.-Nagy, and the reader can therefore refer to these two books.

The author wishes to express his deepest gratitude to L. A. Lyusternik for repeated discussions on the material of the book and for a number of valuable suggestions that have been incorporated in the text.

Contents

CHAPTER I

Approximation of Bounded Linear Operators

1. Abstract Hilbert Space

A set of elements $x, y, z, \ldots$ which possesses the following two properties is called an *abstract Hilbert space* and will be denoted by H:

1. H is a *linear* space, that is, the operations of addition and of multiplication by real or complex numbers are defined for its elements, and these operations obey the usual rules of vector algebra. In particular, H contains an element 0 which is equal to $0 \cdot x$ for every element x in H.

2. H is a *metric* space, in which the metric is introduced with the help of a scalar product. The latter means that with every pair of elements x, y there is associated a real or complex number called their scalar product and denoted by (x, y) such that the following rules are satisfied: $(ax, y) = a(x, y)$ for every number a; $(x + y, z) = (x, z) + (y, z)$; $(x, y) = \overline{(y, x)}$; $(x, x) > 0$ for $x \neq 0$ and $(x, x) = 0$ for $x = 0$.

The *norm* of an element x is then defined by

$$\| x \| = \sqrt{(x, x)},$$

and the distance between x and y by $\| x - y \|$. The norm of an element other than the zero element is positive.

If $(x, y) = 0$, so is (y, x), and in that event the elements are said to be *orthogonal* $(x \perp y)$.

An example of a Hilbert space would be that of ordinary three-dimensional vector space whose elements are vectors defined by three components in some coordinate system. The addition of two vectors x, y with respective components x_1, x_2, x_3 and y_1, y_2, y_3 and multiplication by a scalar are performed according to the rules of vector algebra. That is, if

$$z = ax + by,$$

then $\qquad z_1 = ax_1 + by_1, \quad z_2 = ax_2 + by_2, \quad z_3 = ax_3 + by_3.$

The scalar product is the sum of the products of respective components:

$$(x, y) = x_1 y_1 + x_2 y_2 + x_3 y_3,$$

and the norm of a vector is its length:

$$\| x \| = \sqrt{(x_1^2 + x_2^2 + x_3^2)}.$$

The zero element is the vector whose components are all zero.

A natural generalization of this space is (complex) n-dimensional vector space H_n whose elements x are vectors given by sets of (complex) numbers $x_1, x_2, \dots, x_n$ again called components. The operations of addition and multiplication by a scalar are defined in the usual way: if $z = ax + by$, then $z_i = ax_i + by_i$ $(i = 1, 2, \dots, n)$.

The scalar product is defined by

$$(x, y) = \sum_{i=1}^{n} x_i \bar{y}_i,$$

and the norm by

$$\| x \| = \sqrt{\left(\sum_{i=1}^{n} | x_i |^2 \right)}.$$

The zero element is again the vector with all zero components.

Sometimes weight factors are introduced in the definition of scalar product, and one sets

$$(x, y) = \sum_{i=1}^{n} \rho_i x_i \bar{y}_i, \quad \| x \|^2 = \sum_{i=1}^{n} \rho_i | x_i |^2, \quad \rho_i > 0.$$

Parallel with the notion of a finite dimensional vector space is that of an infinite dimensional vector space l_2 whose elements are infinite sequences of complex numbers $x_1, x_2, \dots$ such that

$$\sum_{i=1}^{\infty} | x_i |^2$$

converges. The numbers $x_1, x_2, \dots$ may be thought of as components of an infinite dimensional vector x in some coordinate system. The addition of elements, multiplication by a scalar, and scalar product are defined exactly as for finite dimensional spaces with the added fact that the series

$$(x, y) = \sum_{i=1}^{\infty} x_i \bar{y}_i$$

will always converge if x and y belong to l_2, that is, if

$$\sum_{i=1}^{\infty} |x_i|^2 \quad \text{and} \quad \sum_{i=1}^{\infty} |y_i|^2$$

converge. The norm is defined in a similar way:

$$\|x\| = \sqrt{\left(\sum_{i=1}^{\infty} |x_i|^2\right)}.$$

Another example of Hilbert space is L_2 function space consisting of functions $x(t)$ (generally speaking, complex) defined and square integrable over an interval $[a,b]$, i.e., for which

$$\int_a^b |x(t)|^2\, dt < \infty.$$

In general, integrability (summability) will be understood to be in the Lebesgue sense, but in applications we shall usually be dealing with ordinary Riemann integrals.

Addition and multiplication by a scalar in L_2 space are carried out according to the usual rules for addition and multiplication of functions. The scalar product and norm are given by

$$(x, y) = \int_a^b x(t)\bar{y}(t)\, dt, \qquad \|x\| = \sqrt{\left(\int_{a]}^b |x(t)|^2\, dt\right)}.$$

We again consider abstract Hilbert space and derive several properties of the scalar product and norm.

Let x and y be elements of H. For any real λ, we have

$$0 \leq \|x + \lambda(x, y)\, y\|^2 = [x + \lambda(x, y)\, y, x + \lambda(x, y)\, y]$$

$$= (x, x) + [x, \lambda(x, y)\, y] + [\lambda(x, y)\, y, x] + \lambda^2[(x, y)\, y, (x, y)\, y].$$

From the definition of scalar product and the fact that λ is real, it follows that

$$[x, \lambda(x, y)\, y] = \lambda(\overline{x, y})(x, y) = \lambda |(x, y)|^2,$$

$$[\lambda(x, y)\, y, x] = \lambda(x, y)(\overline{x, y}) = \lambda |(x, y)|^2,$$

$$[(x, y)\, y, (x, y)\, y] = (x, y)(\overline{x, y})(y, y) = |(x, y)|^2 \|y\|^2.$$

Now, it is readily seen that

$$\|x\|^2 + 2\lambda |(x, y)|^2 + \lambda^2 |(x, y)|^2 \|y\|^2 = \|x + \lambda(x, y)\, y\|^2$$

is a non-negative second degree polynomial in λ and hence cannot have distinct real roots. Therefore its discriminant is non-positive:

$$|(x,y)|^4 - \|x\|^2 \|y\|^2 |(x,y)|^2 \leq 0.$$

Thus

$$|(x,y)|^2 \leq \|x\|^2 \|y\|^2$$

(even when $(x,y) = 0$), or

$$|(x,y)| \leq \|x\| \|y\|. \tag{1}$$

This is *Schwarz's inequality*.

In three-dimensional vector space where the norm of a vector is its length and the scalar product is the product of the lengths of the vectors by the cosine of the angle between them, Schwarz's inequality expresses the simple fact that the cosine of an angle is numerically less than or equal to one.

Consider now the square of the norm of $x+y$:

$$\|x+y\|^2 = (x+y, x+y) = \|x\|^2 + \|y\|^2 + (x,y) + (y,x).$$

Taking into consideration that $|(x,y)+(y,x)| \leq 2|(x,y)|$ and using the inequality (1), we may write

$$\|x+y\|^2 \leq \|x\|^2 + \|y\|^2 + 2\|x\| \|y\|,$$

or

$$\|x+y\| \leq \|x\| + \|y\|. \tag{2}$$

This is the *triangle* inequality which in ordinary vector space expresses the fact that the length of any side of a triangle never exceeds the sum of the lengths of the other two sides.

The application of (2) to the sum $x-y = (x-z)+(z-y)$ yields the formula

$$\|x-y\| \leq \|x-z\| + \|z-y\|. \tag{3}$$

In the further development of the theory, an important part is played by the concept of linear dependence. A set of elements $z_1, z_2 \ldots z_n$ of Hilbert space is *linear dependent* if there exist scalars $a_1, a_2, \ldots, a_n$, not all zero, such that

$$a_1 z_1 + a_2 z_2 + \ldots + a_n z_n = 0.$$

On the other hand the elements are *linearly independent* if this last equality holds only with

$$a_1 = a_2 = \ldots = a_n = 0.$$

In order for the elements $z_1, z_2, \ldots, z_n$ to be linearly independent it is necessary and sufficient that the Gramian

$$\begin{vmatrix} (z_1, z_1), & (z_1, z_2), & \ldots, & (z_1, z_n) \\ (z_2, z_1), & (z_2, z_2), & \ldots, & (z_2, z_n) \\ \cdot \quad \cdot \quad \cdot \quad \cdot \quad \cdot \quad \cdot \quad \cdot \quad \cdot \quad \cdot \quad \cdot \\ (z_n, z_1), & (z_n, z_2), & \ldots, & (z_n, z_n) \end{vmatrix}$$

be different from zero. It is possible to show that the Gramian assumes only non-negative values.

We next introduce the notion of limit. Let $x_1, x_2, \ldots, x_n, \ldots$ be a sequence of elements in H. The sequence is said to *converge* or *tend* (*strongly*) to x if x belongs to H and

$$\| x_n - x \| \underset{n \to \infty}{\to} 0. \tag{4}$$

The element x is called the limit of the sequence $\{x_n\}$. To indicate this, we make use of the standard notation

$$x_n \Rightarrow x \quad \text{or} \quad \lim_{n \to \infty} x_n = x.$$

Let us explain the definition by means of examples.

(a) In vector space, $x_n \Rightarrow x$ is equivalent to

$$\sum_{k=1}^{N} (x_{n,k} - x_k)^2 \to 0, \quad n \to \infty,$$

where $x_{n,k}$ are the components of x_n and N is the dimension of the space. Hence, it follows that $x_{n,k} \to x_k$ in the usual sense.

(b) In L_2 space, $x_n \Rightarrow x$ means that

$$\int_a^b [x_n(t) - x(t)]^2 \, dt \to 0, \quad n \to \infty.$$

This type of convergence is known as *mean* convergence. We note that mean convergence certainly does not imply ordinary convergence even when $x(t)$ and $x_n(t)$ are continuous.

If $x_n \Rightarrow x$ and $y_n \Rightarrow y$ then $(x_n \ y_n) \to (x \ y)$. For, it is easy to show that

$$(x_n, y_n) - (x, y) = (x_n - x, y_n - y) + (x, y_n - y) + (x_n - x, y).$$

Hence, by the Schwarz inequality,

$$|(x_n, y_n)-(x, y)|$$
$$\leq \| x_n-x \| \| y_n-y \| + \| x \| \| y_n-y \| + \| y \| \| x_n-x \| \to 0,$$

q.e.d.

The convergence of x_n to x further implies the convergence of (x_n, y) to (x, y) for any y as well as the convergence of $\| x_n \|$ to $\| x \|$. We again consider the general concept of convergence.

Suppose $\{x_n\}$ is a given convergent sequence with limit x in H. By definition, $\| x_n-x \| \to 0$. Making use of the triangle inequality (3), we obtain

$$\| x_m-x_n \| = \| (x_m-x)-(x_n-x) \| \leq \| x_m-x \| + \| x_n-x \|.$$

The right-hand side tends to zeio as n and m approach infinity, or in other words,

$$\lim_{\substack{n\to\infty\\m\to\infty}} \| x_n-x_m \| = 0. \tag{5}$$

Thus, if $x_n \Rightarrow x$, then the relation (5) necessarily holds. The converse statement is in general false. Namely, if (5) is satisfied, the limit of the sequence $\{x_n\}$ may prove to not belong to the considered Hilbert space.

A Hilbert space H is said to be complete if every sequence of its elements satisfying the relation (5) possesses a limit in H.

An incomplete Hilbert space can be made complete by the adjunction to it of certain new elements in the same manner in which the set of rational numbers is enlarged into the real numbers by the introduction of the irrationals.

Suppose a sequence $\{x_n\}$ satisfies (5) but has no limit in H. The sequence is then assigned a new so-called *ideal* element x as its limit. If x and y are two ideal elements defined by the respective sequences $\{x_n\}$ and $\{y_n\}$, then x and y are assumed equal if

$$\lim_{n\to\infty} \| x_n-y_n \| = 0.$$

The scalar product of ideal elements is defined by

$$(x, y) = \lim_{n\to\infty} (x_n, y_n),$$

and
$$\| x \| = \lim_{n\to\infty} \| x_n \|.$$

The existence of the limits of these numerical sequences is easy to establish.

The adjunction to H of all its ideal elements makes H complete. This process is called *closure* or *completion* of the space.

The above-mentioned finite dimensional space H_n, infinite dimensional space l_2, and function space L_2 are all complete Hilbert spaces.

Henceforth, whenever we speak of a Hilbert space, we shall always assume it to be complete.

We now introduce a few concepts concerning sets of elements in H. A subset L is called a linear manifold if whenever any elements $x_1, x_2, \ldots, x_m$ are in L, every linear combination of them $a_1 x_1 + a_2 x_2 + \ldots + a_m x_m$ is also contained in L. Furthermore, if the limit of every convergent sequence of elements of L is in L, i.e., L contains all its ideal elements, then the linear manifold is a *subspace*.

Every linear manifold in H_n is complete and hence a subspace. Examples of subspaces in ordinary (real) three-dimensional vector space would be the whole space, and a plane or line passing through the origin.

If x_1 is any element of H and a a complex number, then the set of elements $a x_1$ is a subspace. If $x_1, \ldots, x_n$ are n linearly independent elements and $a_1, a_2, \ldots, a_n$ any complex numbers, then the set of elements $a_1 x_1 + a_2 x_2 + \ldots + a_n x_n$ is also a subspace. All the above examples concern finite dimensional subspaces. However, infinite dimensional subspaces do exist. In any case, a subspace may be regarded as an independent Hilbert space.

We now prove a theorem which is of basic importance in all that follows.

Theorem I. *If L is a subspace of H, then every element x in H can be represented uniquely in the form*

$$x = y + z, \tag{6}$$

where y belongs to L ($y \in L$) and z is orthogonal to $L (z \perp L)$.

If $x \in L$, the statement is obviously true. Suppose that x does not belong to L. Let d be the infimum of the set of positive numbers $\| x - y \|^2$, where y runs through the entire subspace L. A sequence of elements y_n then exists in L such that

$$\| x - y_n \|^2 = (x - y_n, x - y_n) = d_n \to d.$$

Suppose now that u is any element of L; then $y_n + \varepsilon u$ also belongs to L.

Recalling that d is an infimum, we may write $(x - y_n - \varepsilon u, x - y_n - \varepsilon u) \geqq d$. On carrying out the scalar product, we obtain the inequality

$$(u, u)\varepsilon^2 - \varepsilon[(x - y_n, u) + (u, x - y_n)] + (d_n - d) \geqq 0.$$

Since $(u, x - y_n) = \overline{(x - y_n, u)}$, we have

$$(u, u)\varepsilon^2 - 2\operatorname{Re}(x - y_n, u)\varepsilon + (d_n - d) \geqq 0.$$

The trinomial on the left-hand side is non-negative for real values of ε and hence
$$|\operatorname{Re}(x - y_n, u)| \leqq \sqrt{(d_n - d)} \, \| u \|.$$

This inequality may be strengthened as follows. Let ϕ be the argument of the complex number $(u, x - y_n)$, so that $(u, x - y_n) = |(u, x - y_n)| e^{i\phi}$. Replacing u in the inequality by $ue^{-i\phi}$, also an element of L, and noting that $\| ue^{-i\phi} \| = \| u \|$, we have

$$(ue^{-i\phi}, x - y_n) = e^{-i\phi}(u, x - y_n) = |(u, x - y_n)|,$$

and thus
$$|(u, x - y_n)| \leqq \sqrt{(d_n - d)} \, \| u \|. \tag{7}$$

Recall that the x in this inequality is a prescribed element of H, y_n is a sequence in L such that $\| x - y_n \|^2 \to d$, and u is any element of L.

Let us next estimate the modulus of $(u, y_n - y_m)$. Expressing $y_n - y_m$ in the form $(y_n - x) + (x - y_m)$ and making use of the inequality (7), we find that

$$|(u, y_n - y_m)| \leqq |(u, x - y_n)| + |(u, x - y_m)|$$

$$\leqq [\sqrt{(d_n - d)} + \sqrt{(d_m - d)}] \, \| u \|.$$

The substitution of $u = y_n - y_m$ and cancellation of $\| y_n - y_m \|$ from both sides then leads to the inequality

$$\| y_n - y_m \| \leqq \sqrt{(d_n - d)} + \sqrt{(d_m - d)}.$$

If n and m are allowed to approach infinity, the right-hand side tends to zero and therefore the sequence y_n has a limit y in L by virtue of L being a complete subspace.

Passage to the limit in (7) then leads to the conclusion that for any element u belonging to L.

$$(z, u) = 0, \quad z = x - y.$$

It remains to show that the representation obtained is unique. Suppose there are two such decompositions

$$x = y + z = y_1 + z_1,$$

with y and y_1 in L, and z and z_1 orthogonal to the subspace L. The scalar product of the equation $y - y_1 = z_1 - z$ with $y - y_1$ and $z_1 - z$ respectively yields $\| y - y_1 \| = 0$ and $\| z - z_1 \| = 0$. Hence the theorem is proved.

The element y appearing in (6) and belonging to L is called the *projection of x on the subspace L*.

2. Bounded Linear Operators

An *operator* on H is a correspondence that assigns to every element x in H another specific element y in H. We write this as follows:

$$y = Ax.$$

An operator A carrying elements x of H into elements Ax of the same space is said to be *linear* and *bounded* if it is

(a) additive: $A(x_1 + x_2) = Ax_1 + Ax_2$,

(b) homogeneous: $A(ax) = aAx$, and

(c) bounded: a positive number M exists such that

$$\| Ax \| \leqq M \| x \|.$$

The smallest such number M is called the *norm* of A and is denoted by $\| A \|$.

Every bounded linear operator is continuous in the sense that if a sequence of elements x_n in H converges to x, then the sequence Ax_n converges to Ax; in fact

$$\| Ax - Ax_n \| = \| A(x - x_n) \| \leqq \| A \| \, \| x - x_n \| \to 0.$$

The operations of addition and multiplication of bounded linear operators are defined in an obvious way:

$$(aA)x = aAx, \quad (A + B)x = Ax + Bx, \quad (AB)x = A(Bx).$$

It is then easy to show that

$$\| aA \| = |a| \, \| A \|, \quad \| A + B \| \leqq \| A \| + \| B \|,$$

$$\| AB \| \leqq \| A \| \, \| B \|.$$

In particular, powers of an operator, $A^2 = AA, A^3 = AA^2 = A^2 A, \ldots$ satisfy the inequalities

$$\| A^2 \| \leqq \| A \|^2, \ldots, \| A^n \| \leqq \| A \|^n, \ldots.$$

A few examples of bounded linear operators will now be given.

In n-dimensional vector space, a linear transformation defined by means of a matrix A by

$$y = Ax$$

or explicitly

$$y_k = a_{k1} x_1 + a_{k2} x_2 + \ldots + a_{kn} x_n \quad (k = 1, 2, \ldots, n),$$

where x_k and y_k are the components of x and y, is a linear operator.

It is easy to see that such an operator is bounded. The Schwarz inequality in this space has the form

$$\left| \sum_{k=1}^{n} x_k \bar{y}_k \right|^2 \leq \sum_{k=1}^{n} |x_k|^2 \sum_{k=1}^{n} |y_k|^2.$$

Therefore

$$(Ax, Ax) = \sum_{i=1}^{n} \left| \sum_{k=1}^{n} a_{ik} x_k \right|^2 \leq \sum_{i=1}^{n} \left[\sum_{k=1}^{n} |a_{ik}|^2 \sum_{s=1}^{n} |x_s|^2 \right]$$

$$= \sum_{i,k=1}^{n} |a_{ik}|^2 \sum_{s=1}^{n} |x_s|^2.$$

Thus,

$$\| Ax \|^2 \leq \sum_{i,k=1}^{n} |a_{ik}|^2 \| x \|^2$$

and

$$\| A \| \leq \sqrt{\left(\sum_{i,k=1}^{n} |a_{ik}|^2 \right)}.$$

In infinite dimensional vector space, linear operators are defined by infinite matrices. However, not every infinite matrix defines a bounded operator. If an infinite matrix is such for example that the double series

$$\sum_{i,k=1}^{\infty} |a_{ik}|^2$$

converges, it may then be used to define a bounded linear operator. Just as for a finite dimensional space, it can be shown that

$$\| A \| \leq \sqrt{\left(\sum_{i,k=1}^{\infty} |a_{ik}|^2 \right)}.$$

An example of a linear operator in L_2 space is the integral

$$Ax = \int_a^b K(s,t) x(t) \, dt.$$

This operator is bounded if the following double integral exists:

$$\int_a^b \int_a^b |K(s,t)| \, ds \, dt.$$

The Schwarz inequality (1) is given in L_2 by

$$\left| \int_a^b x(t)y(t) \, dt \right|^2 \leq \int_a^b |x(t)|^2 \, dt \int_a^b |y(t)|^2 \, dt.$$

Applying it to

$$\left[\int_a^b K(s,t)x(t) \, dt \right]^2,$$

we obtain

$$|Ax|^2 \leq \int_a^b |K(s,t)|^2 \, dt \int_a^b |x(t)|^2 \, dt.$$

Integration with respect to s from a to b then yields

$$\|Ax\|^2 \leq \int_a^b \int_a^b |K(s,t)|^2 \, ds \, dt \, \|x\|^2.$$

Thus,

$$\|A\| \leq \sqrt{\left(\int_a^b \int_a^b |K(s,t)|^2 \, ds \, dt \right)}.$$

We next introduce the notions of adjoint and inverse operator.

Let A be a bounded linear operator, and consider the scalar product (Ax,y) for any x and y in the Hilbert space H. The adjoint operator A^* is defined by the relation

$$(Ax, y) = (x, A^*y).$$

It can be shown that this equation completely determines A^* and, moreover, that $(A^*)^* = A$.

A^* is also a bounded operator with the norm $\|A\|$. For,

$$\|A^*x\|^2 = (A^*x, A^*x)$$

$$= (AA^*x, x) \leq \|AA^*x\| \, \|x\| \leq \|A\| \, \|A^*x\| \, \|x\|.$$

Cancelling the common factor $\|A^*x\|$, we obtain

$$\|A^*x\| \leq \|A\| \, \|x\|.$$

(The inequality holds trivially if $\|A^*x\| = 0$). Hence, $\|A^*\| \leq \|A\|$. From the fact that $(A^*)^* = A$, we can also deduce the opposite inequality, $\|A\| \leq \|A^*\|$, and therefore A^* has the same norm as A.

A bounded operator A is called *self-adjoint* if $A = A^*$. Thus, a self-adjoint operator is characterized by the relation

$$(Ax, y) = (x, Ay).$$

If we set $x = y$ and use the fact that $(Ax, x) = \overline{(x, Ax)}$, we can conclude that (Ax, x) is real for a self-adjoint operator. The converse statement also holds.

A concept of basic importance in operator theory is the inverse operator. A linear operator A is said to have a *bounded inverse* if there exists a bounded operator B such that

$$AB = BA = I,$$

where I is the identity operator, that is, $Ix = x$. A bounded inverse operator is unique. For if $AC = I$, then by applying the operator B to both sides and by making use of the fact that $BI = B$, we conclude that $C = B$. The inverse operator is usually denoted by A^{-1}. Thus,

$$AA^{-1} = A^{-1}A = I.$$

Inverse operators play a basic part in the solution of non-homogeneous equations such as

$$Ax = y,$$

where y is a prescribed element and x the unknown. Applying the inverse operator to both sides of this equation, we obtain

$$x = A^{-1}y.$$

Thus, the existence of a bounded inverse operator assures the solvability of a non-homogeneous linear equation for any y in H.

Besides non-homogeneous equations, applications also often lead to homogeneous equations of the form

$$Au = \lambda u,$$

with u the unknown and λ a numerical parameter. The number λ is called an *eigenvalue* of A if the homogeneous equation has corresponding non-trivial solutions; these solutions are called *eigenelements of the operator A*. The number of linearly independent eigenelements correpsonding to an eigenvalue determines its *multiplicity*. An eigenvalue may have infinite multiplicity.

The limit of a sequence of bounded linear operators A_n may be defined in various ways. We shall make use of two types of convergence.

A sequence of bounded linear operators A_n converges to a bounded linear operator A if for every element x in H, the sequence $A_n x$ converges to Ax: $A_n x \Rightarrow Ax$. This is sometimes called strong convergence and will be denoted $A_n \to A$.

The second type of convergence we shall consider is *uniform convergence*.

A sequence of bounded linear operators A_n converges to A uniformly if $\| A - A_n \|_{\overrightarrow{n \to \infty}} 0$. Such convergence is sometimes referred to as *convergence in norm*. Uniform convergence implies strong convergence:

$$\| A_n x - Ax \| \leq \| A_n - A \| \, \| x \| \to 0$$

for any x in H.

In concluding this section, we pause to consider a class of linear operators which we shall frequently use in the following. Let L be a subspace of H. According to Theorem I, every x in H has the unique decomposition $x = y + z$, with $y \in L$ and $z \perp L$. An operator mapping x into its projection y is called a *projection onto the subspace L* and will be denoted by E_L:

$$y = E_L x.$$

Since y and z are orthogonal, we have

$$\| x \|^2 = (y + z, y + z) = \| y \|^2 + \| z \|^2.$$

Hence,
$$\| y \|^2 = \| E_L x \|^2 \leq \| x \|^2.$$

Equality occurs when $x \in L$, and therefore $\| E_L \| = 1$.

If x belongs to L, then clearly $E_L x = x$. Thus, for every x in H, $E_L E_L x = E_L x$ and

$$E_L^2 = E_L.$$

A projection is self-adjoint. For, let x_1 and x_2 be any two elements of H and $x_1 = y_1 + z_1$ and $x_2 = y_2 + z_2$ their respective decompositions according to Theorem I. Form the scalar product $(E_L x_1, x_2)$. By definition, $E_L x_1 = y_1$, and $E_L x_2 = y_2$. Now using the fact that z_1 and z_2 are orthogonal to L, we may write

$$(E_L x_1, x_2) = (E_L x_1, y_2 + z_2) = (y_1, y_2) = (y_1, E_L x_2)$$

$$= (y_1 + z_1, E_L x_2) = (x_1, E_L x_2).$$

Hence E_L is a self-adjoint operator.

Thus far we have considered bounded linear operators acting on all elements of the space H. It is possible to consider an operator as acting on just the elements of some subspace L thus contracting its domain of definition. If in this connection Ax belongs to L whenever x does, then the space L is said to *reduce* the operator A.

The significance of this definition is as follows. Since L is an independent Hilbert space, the fact that L reduces A means that A may be given separate consideration as an operator on L. The analysis of A in the separate subspaces reducing it greatly facilitates the study of A.

3. The Problem of Moments in Hilbert Space

Let $z_0, z_1, \ldots, z_n$ be $n+1$ prescribed linearly independent elements of Hilbert space H. Consider the n-dimensional subspace H_n generated by all possible linear combinations of $z_0, z_1, \ldots, z_{n-1}$.

The problem we wish to solve is the following: To construct a linear operator A_n defined on the subspace H_n such that

$$\left.\begin{aligned}
z_1 &= A_n z_0, \\
z_2 &= A_n z_1, \\
& \cdot \quad \cdot \quad \cdot \quad \cdot \quad \cdot \quad \cdot \\
z_{n-1} &= A_n z_{n-2}, \\
E_n z_n &= A_n z_{n-1},
\end{aligned}\right\} \tag{8}$$

where $E_n z_n$ is the projection of z_n on H_n. The equations (8) can also be written in the form

$$\left.\begin{aligned}
z_k &= A_n^k z_0 \quad (k = 0, 1, \ldots, n-1) \\
E_n z_n &= A_n^n z_0.
\end{aligned}\right\} \tag{8'}$$

Henceforth, this problem will be called the *problem of moments* in Hilbert space.

Strictly speaking, the solution of the problem is contained in its very formulation. In fact, it is easy to see that the equations (8) define A_n completely.

Let $x \in H_n$. By definition of H_n, it may be expressed as

$$x = C_0 z_0 + C_1 z_1 + \ldots + C_{n-1} z_{n-1},$$

where $C_0, C_1, \ldots, C_{n-1}$ are constants. Thus

$$\begin{aligned}
A_n x &= C_0 A_n z_0 + C_1 A_n z_1 + \ldots + C_{n-1} A_n z_{n-1} \\
&= C_0 z_1 + C_1 z_2 + \ldots + C_{n-1} E_n z_n \in H_n.
\end{aligned}$$

We now proceed to study the properties of A_n and first determine its eigenvalues.

Since $E_n z_n$ is an element of the subspace H_n, we can find numbers $\alpha_0, \alpha_1, \ldots, \alpha_{n-1}$ such that

$$E_n z_n = -\alpha_0 z_0 - \alpha_1 z_1 - \ldots - \alpha_{n-1} z_{n-1} \tag{9}$$

and this by the use of (8′) leads to

$$P_n(A_n) z_0 = (A_n^n + \alpha_{n-1} A_n^{n-1} + \ldots + \alpha_0 I) z_0 = 0, \tag{10}$$

with I the identity operator.

Taking the scalar product of (9) successively with $z_0, z_1, \ldots, z_{n-1}$, we obtain a system of linear algebraic equations for the coefficients of the polynomial $P_n(\lambda)$:

$$\left.\begin{aligned}
(z_0, z_0)\alpha_0 + (z_0, z_1)\alpha_1 + \ldots + (z_0, z_{n-1})\alpha_{n-1} + (z_0, z_n) &= 0, \\
(z_1, z_0)\alpha_0 + (z_1, z_1)\alpha_1 + \ldots + (z_1, z_{n-1})\alpha_{n-1} + (z_1, z_n) &= 0, \\
\cdot \quad \cdot \quad \cdot \quad \cdot \quad \cdot \quad \cdot \quad \cdot \quad \cdot \quad \cdot \quad \cdot \quad \cdot \quad \cdot \quad \cdot \quad \cdot \quad \cdot \quad & \\
(z_{n-1}, z_0)\alpha_0 + (z_{n-1}, z_1)\alpha_1 + \ldots + (z_{n-1}, z_{n-1})\alpha_{n-1} + (z_{n-1}, z_n) &= 0.
\end{aligned}\right\} \tag{11}$$

In this, we have made use of the fact that $z_n - E_n z_n$ must be orthogonal to every element of H_n because $E_n z_n$ is the projection of z_n on H_n and hence in particular that

$$(z_n - E_n z_n, z_k) = 0 \quad (k = 0, 1, \ldots, n-1).$$

Therefore $\quad (E_n z_n, z_k) = (z_n, z_k) \quad (k = 0, 1, \ldots, n-1).$

The determinant of the system (11) is the Gramian of $z_0, z_1, \ldots, z_{n-1}$ and so does not vanish by virtue of their linear independence. Thus, the system (11) has a unique solution.

Suppose now that λ is an eigenvalue and u an eigenelement of the operator A_n, that is,

$$A_n u = \lambda u. \tag{12}$$

Since u belongs to the subspace H_n, it is expressible as

$$u = \xi_0 z_0 + \xi_1 z_1 + \ldots + \xi_{n-1} z_{n-1},$$

where $\xi_0, \xi_1, \ldots, \xi_{n-1}$ are scalars. Substituting this into equation (12) and making use of (8) and (9), we obtain

$$-\alpha_0 \xi_{n-1} z_0 + (\xi_0 - \alpha_1 \xi_{n-1}) z_1 + \ldots + (\xi_{n-2} - \alpha_{n-1} \xi_{n-1}) z_{n-1}$$
$$= \lambda(\xi_0 z_0 + \xi_1 z_1 + \ldots + \xi_{n-1} z_{n-1}).$$

Again by the fact that the z_k are linearly independent, we can equate coefficients of like elements; this leads to the following system of equations for λ and the ξ_k:

$$\left.\begin{array}{r}
-\alpha_0\,\xi_{n-1} = \lambda\xi_0, \\[4pt]
\xi_0 - \alpha_1\,\xi_{n-1} = \lambda\xi_1, \\[4pt]
\xi_1 - \alpha_2\,\xi_{n-1} = \lambda\xi_2, \\[4pt]
\cdot \quad \cdot \quad \cdot \quad \cdot \quad \cdot \quad \cdot \quad \cdot \quad \cdot \quad \cdot \\[4pt]
\xi_{n-2} - \alpha_{n-1}\,\xi_{n-1} = \lambda\xi_{n-1}.
\end{array}\right\} \qquad (13)$$

In order for this system to have a non-trivial solution in the ξ_k, its determinant, which is $P_n(\lambda)$, must be equal to zero, and therefore the eigenvalues of A_n are roots of

$$P_n(\lambda) = \lambda^n + \alpha_{n-1}\,\lambda^{n-1} + \ldots + \alpha_0 = 0. \qquad (14)$$

The coefficient ξ_{n-1} automatically differs from zero otherwise in general all ξ_k would vanish, as follows from system (13), and we would have only the trivial solution. Since an eigenvalue is determined to within a factor, we can set $\xi_{n-1} = 1$ and then find the other ξ_k recursively from the formulas

$$\left.\begin{array}{l}
\xi_j = \lambda\xi_{j+1} + \alpha_{j+1} \quad (j = 0, 1, \ldots, n-3), \\[4pt]
\xi_{n-2} = \lambda + \alpha_{n-1}.
\end{array}\right\} \qquad (15)$$

Finally, to each eigenvalue there corresponds but one eigenelement.

The simple structure of the operator A_n enables one also to construct its inverse A_n^{-1} easily. If f is in H_n then by definition of inverse operator, $x = A_n^{-1} f$ satisfies

$$A_n x = f, \qquad (16)$$

(an equation of the *first kind*). Since $f \in H_n$, it may be expressed in the form

$$f = \sum_{k=0}^{n-1} b_k z_k = \sum_{k=0}^{n-1} b_k A_n^k z_0 = F_{n-1}(A_n)z_0,$$

$$F_{n-1}(\lambda) = b_{n-1}\,\lambda^{n-1} + b_{n-2}\,\lambda^{n-2} + \ldots + b_0.$$

By taking the scalar product successively with $z_0, z_1, \ldots, z_{n-1}$, we arrive at a system of linear equations for the coefficients of the polynomial $F_{n-1}(\lambda)$, namely,

$$(z_0, z_0)b_0 + (z_0, z_1)b_1 + \ldots + (z_0, z_{n-1})b_{n-1} - (z_0, f) = 0$$

$$(z_1, z_0)b_0 + (z_1, z_1)b_1 + \ldots + (z_1, z_{n-1})b_{n-1} - (z_1, f) = 0$$

. . . .

$$(z_{n-1}, z_0)b_0 + (z_{n-1}, z_1)b_1 + \ldots + (z_{n-1}, z_{n-1})b_{n-1} - (z_{n-1}, f) = 0.$$

These equations differ from those of system (11) only in their respective last terms.

Because x is in H_n, it may also be expressed in terms of a polynomial in A_n, namely,

$$x = Q_{n-1}(A_n)z_0.$$

The substitution of this in (16) yields

$$[A_n Q_{n-1}(A_n) - F_{n-1}(A_n)]z_0 = 0.$$

Now the polynomial $P_n(A_n)$ is uniquely defined, and thus any n-th degree polynomial in A_n which annihilates z_0 can only differ from $P_n(A_n)$ by a constant factor. Hence,

$$A_n Q_{n-1}(A_n) - F_{n-1}(A_n) = CP_n(A_n).$$

Equating the constant terms, we find for C the value

$$C = -\frac{F_{n-1}(0)}{P_n(0)}.$$

Thus,

$$Q_{n-1}(A_n) = A_n^{-1}\left[F_{n-1}(A_n) - \frac{F_{n-1}(0)}{P_n(0)}P_n(A_n)\right],$$

and the required solution of (16) is given by

$$x = A_n^{-1}\left[F_{n-1}(A_n) - \frac{F_{n-1}(0)}{P_n(0)}P_n(A_n)\right]z_0 \qquad (17)$$

or, on the removal of parentheses,

$$x = A_n^{-1}\left[\left(b_1 - \frac{b_0}{\alpha_0}\alpha_1\right)A_n + \ldots + \left(b_{n-1} - \frac{b_0}{\alpha_0}\alpha_{n-1}\right)A_n^{n-1} - \frac{b_0}{\alpha_0}A_n^n\right]z_0$$

$$= \left(b_1 - \frac{b_0}{\alpha_0}\alpha_1\right)z_0 + \ldots + \left(b_{n-1} - \frac{b_0}{\alpha_0}\alpha_{n-1}\right)z_{n-2} - \frac{b_0}{\alpha_0}z_{n-1}. \qquad (17')$$

Equation (17) [or (17′)] determines the inverse operator. Clearly, in order for it to exist, $P_n(0) = \alpha_0 \neq 0$, that is, zero should not be an eigenvalue of A_n.

Besides equations such as (16), one also encounters equations of the *second kind*

$$x = \mu A_n x + f, \tag{18}$$

where μ is a parameter.

The solution of any such equation may be obtained in a completely similar way. Setting $x = Q_{n-1}(A_n)z_0$ and $f = F_{n-1}(A_n)z_0$ in equation (18), we arrive at

$$[Q_{n-1}(A_n) - \mu A_n Q_{n-1}(A_n) - F_{n-1}(A_n)]z_0 = 0,$$

or $\qquad (1 - \mu\lambda)Q_{n-1}(\lambda) - F_{n-1}(\lambda) = CP_n(\lambda). \tag{19}$

Letting $\lambda = 1/\mu$, we now find for C the value

$$C = -\frac{F_{n-1}\left(\dfrac{1}{\mu}\right)}{P_n\left(\dfrac{1}{\mu}\right)}.$$

Thus, $\qquad Q_{n-1}(A_n) = (I - \mu A_n)^{-1}\left[F_{n-1}(A_n) - \dfrac{F_{n-1}\left(\dfrac{1}{\mu}\right)}{P_n\left(\dfrac{1}{\mu}\right)}P_n(A_n)\right],$

and the solution to equation (18) is given by

$$x = (I - \mu A_n)^{-1}\left[F_{n-1}(A_n) - \frac{F_{n-1}\left(\dfrac{1}{\mu}\right)}{P_n\left(\dfrac{1}{\mu}\right)}P_n(A_n)\right]z_0. \tag{20}$$

The solution may also be expressed explicitly in terms of the basis elements $z_0, z_1, \ldots, z_{n-1}$. The substitution of

$$Q_{n-1}(\lambda) = a_{n-1}\lambda^{n-1} + a_{n-2}\lambda^{n-2} + \ldots + a_0 = \sum_{k=0}^{n-1} a_k \lambda^k,$$

$$F_{n-1}(\lambda) = b_{n-1}\lambda^{n-1} + b_{n-2}\lambda^{n-2} + \ldots + b_0 = \sum_{k=0}^{n-1} b_k \lambda,$$

$$P_n(\lambda) = \lambda^n + \alpha_{n-1}\lambda^{n-1} + \ldots + \alpha_0 = \sum_{k=0}^{n} \alpha_k \lambda^k$$

in equation (19) yields

$$\sum_{k=0}^{n-1} a_k \lambda^k - \mu \sum_{k=0}^{n-1} a_k \lambda^{k+1} = \sum_{k=0}^{n-1} b_k \lambda^k + C \sum_{k=0}^{n} \alpha_k \lambda^k.$$

But

$$\sum_{k=0}^{n-1} a_k \lambda^{k+1} = \sum_{k=1}^{n} a_{k-1} \lambda^k,$$

and therefore,

$$a_0 - b_0 - C\alpha_0 + \sum_{k=1}^{n-1} (a_k - \mu a_{k-1} - b_k - C\alpha_k)\lambda^k - (\mu a_{n-1} + C)\lambda^n \equiv 0.$$

If the coefficients of like powers of λ are equated to zero and the value of C inserted, we obtain recursion formulas for the coefficients of the polynomial $Q_{n-1}(\lambda)$:

$$\left.\begin{array}{l} a_0 = b_0 - \dfrac{F_{n-1}\left(\dfrac{1}{\mu}\right)}{P_n\left(\dfrac{1}{\mu}\right)} \alpha_0, \\[3em] a_k = \mu a_{k-1} + b_k - \dfrac{F_{n-1}\left(\dfrac{1}{\mu}\right)}{P_n\left(\dfrac{1}{\mu}\right)} \alpha_k \quad (k = 1, 2, \ldots, n-1). \end{array}\right\} \tag{21}$$

The coefficient of λ^n is automatically zero because of our choice of C.

After the computation of the a_k from these recursion formulas, the solution of equation (18) may be written out as

$$x = Q_{n-1}(A_n)z_0 = a_0 z_0 + a_1 z_1 + \ldots + a_{n-1} z_{n-1}. \tag{20'}$$

It exists provided μ^{-1} is not a root of the polynomial $P_n(\lambda)$, or in other words, if μ^{-1} is not an eigenvalue of the operator A_n.

4. Approximation of Bounded Linear Operators

We now show how a sequence of operators A_n may be constructed iteratively so as to converge to a preassigned bounded operator.

Suppose that A is a bounded linear operator in Hilbert space H. Choosing an element z_0, we first form a sequence of iterations using the operator A as follows:

$$z_0, \quad z_1 = Az_0, \quad z_2 = Az_1 = A^2 z_0, \ldots, z_n = Az_{n-1} = A^n z_0, \ldots$$

For the present, $z_0, z_1, \ldots, z_n$ are assumed to be linearly independent.

By solving the moment problem, we thus determine a sequence of operators A_n each defined on its own subspace H_n generated by all linear combinations of $z_0, z_1, \ldots, z_{n-1}$.

The spaces expand with increasing n, and H_{n+1} contains H_n.

The formulas (8') assume the form

$$
\left.
\begin{aligned}
z_k &= A^k z_0 = A_n^k z_0 \quad (k = 0, 1, \ldots, n-1), \\
E_n z_n &= E_n A^n z_0 = A_n^n z_0,
\end{aligned}
\right\} \tag{22}
$$

with $E_n A^n z_0$ the projection of $A^n z_0$ on the subspace H_n.

Next, let E_n be the operator projecting onto the subspace H_n. It is easy to show that

$$
A_n = E_n A E_n. \tag{23}
$$

In fact, take any x in H_n:

$$
x = \sum_{k=0}^{n-1} a_k z_k.
$$

By definition, $E_n x = x$, and therefore

$$
A E_n x = \sum_{k=0}^{n-1} a_k A z_k.
$$

Applying (22), we obtain

$$
A E_n x = \sum_{k=0}^{n-1} a_k A^{k+1} z_0 = \sum_{k=0}^{n-2} a_k A_n^{k+1} z_0 + a_{n-1} A^n z_0.
$$

Projecting this onto H_n, we finally have

$$
E_n A E_n x = \sum_{k=0}^{n-2} a_k A_n^{k+1} z_0 + a_{n-1} E_n A^n z_0 = \sum_{k=0}^{n-1} a_k A_n^{k+1} z_0
$$

$$
= \sum_{k=0}^{n-1} a_k A_n z_k = A_n x.
$$

The effect of relation (23) is to extend the domain of the operator A_n to the whole space H. Furthermore, the relation implies the very important fact that the A_n are uniformly bounded with

$$
\| A_n \| \le \| A \|. \tag{24}
$$

Now consider a linear manifold L_z consisting of elements of the form

$$
x = Q(A) z_0,
$$

where $Q(\lambda)$ is an arbitrary polynomial, and adjoin all its ideal elements so as to form a subspace H_z. This subspace reduces the operator A. For, if $x = Q(A)z_0 \in L_z$, then $Ax = AQ(A)z_0 \in L_z$ also. On the other hand, if x is an ideal element of L_z, then a sequence $x_n = Q_n(A)z_0 \in L_z$ exists such that

$$\| x - x_n \| \to 0.$$

But then
$$\| Ax - Ax_n \| \leq \| A \| \| x - x_n \| \to 0,$$

and since $Ax_n \in L_z$, this implies that Ax, the limit of elements of L_z, must belong to H_z. Thus, A can be considered to be an operator on H_z.

Basic in the method of moments is

Theorem II: *If A is a bounded linear operator and A_n a sequence of solutions of the problem of moments* (22), *then the sequence A_n converges strongly to A in the subspace H_z.*

Proof: If $x = Q(A)z_0 \in L_z$, then in view of (22), $Ax = A_n x$ for every n exceeding the degree of the polynomial $Q(\lambda)$ by two. Now let x be an ideal element and $\{x_m\}$ a sequence of elements in L_z converging to it. Then by (24)

$$\| Ax - A_n x \| \leq \| Ax - Ax_m \| + \| Ax_m - A_n x_m \|$$
$$+ \| A_n x_m - A_n x \| \leq 2 \| A \| \| x - x_m \| + \| A_n x_m - Ax_m \|.$$

The first term on the right-hand side may be made arbitrarily small by choosing m sufficiently large, whereas since x_m is in L_z, the second term is simply zero for n sufficiently large. Thus,

$$\| Ax - A_n x \| \to 0, \quad n \to \infty.$$

Thus far, we have assumed that the elements z_k are linearly independent. The case where they are linearly dependent is comparatively easy to handle. For definiteness, suppose that z_n is linearly dependent on $z_0, z_1, \ldots, z_{n-1}$, which implies that $z_n = E_n z_n$ is also in H_n. It is easy to see that the subspace H_n coincides with H_z and reduces the operator A, or in other words, if

$$x = \sum_{k=0}^{n-1} a_k z_k \in H_n,$$

then so does
$$Ax = \sum_{k=0}^{n-1} a_k z_{k+1}.$$

Therefore, in this case, A is an operator on H_n where it coincides with A_n. This is an immediate consequence of (22).

The fact that it is possible to approximate bounded linear operators by operators like A_n means that they can be used to obtain approximate solutions to various linear problems.

When we investigate this question, we shall confine our considerations to two of the most important classes of operators, namely, completely continuous and self-adjoint operators.

The representation of A_n in the form (23) shows that the method of moments falls within the general framework of Galerkin's method as it is understood today.

The abstract scheme of Galerkin's method for operators defined on a Hilbert space H is as follows. Suppose there exists a system of linearly independent elements $\{\phi_k\}$ in H such that every x in H is uniquely representable by a convergent series of the form

$$x = \sum_{i=1}^{\infty} a_k \phi_k,$$

where the coefficients a_k depend on x. Let P_n be a projection defined by

$$P_n x = \sum_{i=1}^{n} a_k \phi_k. \tag{25}$$

The solution of problems by Galerkin's method entails replacing an operator (not necessarily linear) appearing in an equation by an approximation. If B is an operator on H, then the approximate operator is

$$B_n = P_n B P_n. \tag{26}$$

Such approximations of operators in function space lead to systems of algebraic equations.

An examination of formulas (23) and (26) shows that the method of moments differs merely in the choice of the projections E_n.

The first general results on the convergence of the approximations in Galerkin's method were obtained by M. Keldysh [1], his work being based on an analysis of infinite determinants. In subsequent papers, L. Kantorovich [3], S. Mikhlin [1], N. Polsky [1], and M. Krasnoselsky [2] made use of functional analysis. As a rule, they reduced their investigations to a study of completely continuous linear or non-linear operators. In the papers of Polsky and Krasnoselsky, general estimates are given for the speed of convergence of Galerkin's method.

Since the method of moments is contained within Galerkin's method, a number of theorems on the strong convergence of the approximate solutions to be proved in the next chapter are a consequence of general convergence theorems for Galerkin's method.

Success in applying Galerkin's method depends entirely on the choice of the system of elements $\{\phi_k\}$ going into the expansion. In the moments method, we suggest a specific but sufficiently general choice of elements $\phi_k = z_k$ closely connected with the problem being studied that results, as we shall see later on, in a rapidly convergent sequence of approximations.

Moreover, the choice of expansion elements is such as to permit the application of the moments method to problems where it is doubtful whether the Galerkin method may be used. In particular, this concerns oscillation problems involving systems with a finite number of degrees of freedom which are to be studied in Chapter V.

CHAPTER II

Equations With Completely Continuous Operators

I. The Problem of Moments for Completely Continuous Operators

An operator A is said to be *degenerate* if it can be represented in the form

$$Ax = \sum_{k=1}^{n} (x, \psi_k)\phi_k,$$

with n finite and ϕ_k, ψ_k given elements of the considered Hilbert space. A is then called *completely continuous* if for any positive number ε, it can be represented as

$$Ax = A'_\varepsilon x + A''_\varepsilon x,$$

where A'_ε is a degenerate operator and $\| A''_\varepsilon \| < \varepsilon$.

A completely continuous operator is bounded. For, let

$$A'_\varepsilon x = \sum_{k=1}^{n} (x, \psi_k)\phi_k.$$

Then

$$\| Ax \| \leq \sum_{k=1}^{n} |(x, \psi_k)| \, \| \phi_k \| + \varepsilon \| x \| \leq \left(\sum_{k=1}^{n} \| \psi_k \| \, \| \phi_k \| + \varepsilon \right) \| x \|.$$

Hence,
$$\| A \| \leq \sum_{k=1}^{n} \| \psi_k \| \, \| \phi_k \| + \varepsilon.$$

Let us give some examples of completely continuous operators.

In finite dimensional space H_n, every linear operator is degenerate and therefore completely continuous. In fact, every operator A in H_n is given by a linear transformation

$$y = Ax$$

$$y_1 = a_{11}x_1 + a_{12}x_2 + \ldots + a_{1n}x_n$$

$$y_2 = a_{21}x_1 + a_{22}x_2 + \ldots + a_{2n}x_n$$

. . . .

$$y_n = a_{n1}x_1 + a_{n2}x_2 + \ldots + a_{nn}x_n.$$

It is now easy to see that if we set $\psi_k = (a_{k1}, a_{k2}, \ldots, a_{kn})$, $\phi_1 = (1, 0, \ldots, 0)$, $\ldots, \phi_n = (0, \ldots, 0, 1)$, then A can be represented in the form of a degenerate operator

$$Ax = \sum_{k=1}^{n} (x, \psi_k)\phi_k.$$

In the infinite dimensional space l_2, any infinite matrix whose entries are such that

$$\sum_{i,k=1}^{\infty} |a_{i,k}|^2 < \infty,$$

defines a completely continuous operator.

Similarly, in L_2 space, the integral operator

$$Ax = \int_a^b K(s,t)x(t)\,dt$$

is completely continuous if its kernel is square integrable, that is,

$$\int_a^b \int_a^b |K(s,t)|^2\,ds\,dt < \infty.$$

The proof of the complete continuity of the above two operators may be found in the references mentioned in the preface.

The following is a theorem on completely continuous operators which we shall make use of in the sequel and which we state without proof.

Theorem III: *An operator A is completely continuous if and only if every infinite sequence of elements whose norms are uniformly bounded contains a subsequence x_n for which the sequence Ax_n is convergent.*

We now return to the problem of moments.

When the given operator A is completely continuous, Theorem II may be strengthened to the following:

Theorem IV: *If A is a completely continuous operator, then the* *sequence of operators A_n solving the problem of moments* (22) *Chapter I, converges in norm to A in the subspace H_z*:

$$\| A - A_n \| \to 0, \quad n \to \infty.$$

Let E_n be the projection mapping H_z on H_n. We note some of its properties:

$$E_n = E_n^*, \quad \| E_n \| = 1, \quad \| I - E_n \| = 1, \quad E_n \to I.$$

The last property is an immediate consequence of the sequence $A_n z_0$ having a limit in H_z. For, if x is any element of H_z, then by definition we can find a sequence of elements x_n of the form

$$x_n = \sum_{k=0}^{n-1} c_k A^k z_0,$$

such that $\| x - x_n \| \to 0$ when $n \to \infty$. On the other hand, by the projection property, we have

$$\| x - E_n x \| \leq \| x - x_n \| \to 0,$$

and since x is arbitrary, it follows that $E_n \to I$ in H_z.

The theorem will be proved by contradiction. Suppose the theorem to be false and that $\| A - A_n \|$ does not approach zero when $n \to \infty$. Then there exists a sequence of normalized elements f_n in H_z ($\| f_n \| = 1$) such that for arbitrarily large n

$$\| (A - A_n) f_n \| \geq q,$$

where q is a positive number independent of n.

Since A is completely continuous, by Theorem III a convergent subsequence $\{ A f_{n_j} \}$ may be chosen from the sequence $\{ A f_n \}$. By the very same reason, a convergent subsequence may again be selected from the sequence $\{ A(I - E_n) f_{n_j} \}$. There is no loss of generality if it is assumed that f_n is precisely the subsequence mapped into the convergent subsequences by the indicated operators. Denote

$$g = \lim A f_n,$$

$$h = \lim A(I - E_n) f_n,$$

and consider the identity

$$A - A_n = A - E_n A E_n = (I - E_n) A + E_n A(I - E_n).$$

Since

$$\| (I-E_n)Af_n \| \leqq \| (I-E_n)(Af_n-g) \| + \| (I-E_n)g \|$$

$$\leqq \| Af_n-g \| + \| g-E_n g \| \to 0,$$

$$\| E_n A(I-E_n)f_n \| \leqq \| A(I-E_n)f_n \| \to \| h \|$$

and

$$\| h \|^2 = \lim [A(I-E_n)f_n, h] = \lim [f_n, (I-E_n)A^* h]$$

$$\leqq \lim \| (I-E_n)A^* h \| = 0,$$

it follows that

$$\| (A-A_n)f_n \| \to 0,$$

This contradicts our assumption, and hence the theorem is proved.

2. Non-homogeneous Equations with Completely Continuous Operators

In this section, we show how the problem of moments can be used in the actual solution of non-homogeneous linear equations with completely continuous operators.

Consider the equation

$$x = \mu Ax + f, \tag{1}$$

with x the unknown, f a given element of some Hilbert space H, A a completely continuous operator on H, and μ a parameter.

The Fredholm alternative remains valid for such equations: Either the non-homogeneous equation has a unique solution for each prescribed f, in particular, the homogeneous equation ($f=0$) only the trivial solution $x=0$; or the non-homogeneous equation cannot be solved for a given f and the associated homogeneous equation then has non-trivial solutions. The first part of the alternative holds if μ is a regular value and the second if μ is a reciprocal eigenvalue. Whenever μ is regular, there exists a bounded inverse operator $(I-\mu A)^{-1}$.

Equation (1) always possesses a solution if μ is sufficiently small, namely, the following theorem of Banach holds.

Theorem V: *If $|\mu| < \|A\|^{-1}$, the equation* (1) *has a solution for each given f.*

The proof is rather simple. Consider the series

$$f + \mu Af + \mu^2 A^2 f + \dots$$

and let $x^{(n)}$ denote its n-th partial sum. Then since $|\mu|\,\|A\| < 1$,

$$\|x^{(n)} - x^{(m)}\| = \|\mu^m A^m f + \mu^{m+1} A^{m+1} f + \ldots + \mu^{n-1} A^{n-1} f\|$$

$$\leq (|\mu|^m \|A\|^m + |\mu|^{m+1} \|A\|^{m+1} + \ldots + |\mu|^{n-1} \|A\|^{n-1}) \|f\| \to 0$$

when n and m approach infinity. But H is complete, and so the sequence $x^{(n)}$ has a limit x in H. It is easy to show that x is a solution of equation (1). In fact, $\mu A x = \mu A f + \mu^2 A^2 f + \ldots = x - f$ and hence

$$x = \mu A x + f.$$

It should be noted that the theorem is valid for any bounded operator.

To solve (1) with μ a regular value, we apply the method of moments. We first set $z_0 = f$, and form the sequence of iterations

$$z_0 = f, \quad z_1 = Af, \ldots, z_n = A^n f, \ldots.$$

We then replace equation (1) by the "approximate" equation

$$x_n = \mu A_n x_n + f, \tag{2}$$

with A_n the solution of the problem of moments (22), Chapter I.

The solution of this equation was obtained in Chapter I, and in the present case assumes the form

$$x_n = a_0 f + a_1 Af + \ldots + a_{n-1} A^{n-1} f,$$

where the a_k are determined recursively by means of the formulas

$$a_0 = 1 - \frac{\alpha_0}{P_n\left(\dfrac{1}{\mu}\right)},$$

$$a_k = \mu a_{k-1} - \frac{\alpha_k}{P_n\left(\dfrac{1}{\mu}\right)} \qquad (k = 1, 2, \ldots, n-1)$$

The quantities α_k are the coefficients of the polynomial

$$P_n(\lambda) = \lambda^n + \alpha_{n-1} \lambda^{n-1} + \ldots + \alpha_0$$

and satisfy the system (11), Chapter I. Of course as n changes, so do the a_k and α_k.

The following theorem concerning the approximate solution x_n holds.

Theorem VI: *If a solution to (1) exists for each f in H, that is, μ is a* *regular value of the equation, and if A is completely continuous, then for n sufficiently large the equation* (2) *has a solution and the sequence* x_n *converges (strongly) to the solution of* (1).

In proving the theorem, we use a method due to Schmidt. We first write equation (2) in the form

$$x_n - \mu A x_n + \mu(A - A_n)x_n = f.$$

By assumption, the operator $(I - \mu A)^{-1}$ exists and is bounded. Applying it to both sides of the equation, we obtain

$$x_n - \mu(I - \mu A)^{-1}(A_n - A)x_n = (I - \mu A)^{-1}f = x. \qquad (3)$$

According to Banach's Theorem, a solution to this equation exists if

$$\| \mu(I - \mu A)^{-1}(A_n - A) \| < 1. \qquad (4)$$

Now $\quad \| \mu(I - \mu A)^{-1}(A_n - A) \| \leq |\mu| \, \| (I - \mu A)^{-1} \| \, \| A - A_n \|.$

The last factor on the right-hand side tends to zero because the sequence of operators A_n converges to A uniformly. Therefore, condition (4) will be satisfied if n is sufficiently large. The existence of a solution to (2) is thus proved. In order to establish the second part of the theorem, we start from the following decomposition of the inverse operator:

$$(I - \mu A_n)^{-1} = [I - \mu(I - \mu A)^{-1}(A_n - A)]^{-1}(I - \mu A)^{-1}.$$

Expanding in powers of μ, we obtain

$$[I - \mu(I - \mu A)^{-1}(A_n - A)]^{-1} = \sum_{k=0}^{\infty} \mu^k [(I - \mu A)^{-1}(A_n - A)]^k.$$

This is a convergent series since for sufficiently large n

$$\| \mu(I - \mu A)^{-1}(A_n - A) \| < 1.$$

The sequence of operators $(I - \mu A_n)^{-1}$ is uniformly bounded for n sufficiently large inasmuch as

$$\| (I - \mu A_n)^{-1} \| \leq \| (I - \mu A)^{-1} \| \sum_{k=0}^{\infty} |\mu|^k \, \| (I - \mu A)^{-1} \|^k \, \| A - A_n \|^k$$

$$= \frac{\| (I - \mu A)^{-1} \|}{1 - |\mu| \, \| (I - \mu A)^{-1} \| \, \| A - A_n \|}$$

and $\| A - A_n \| \to 0$.

We now show that the sequence $(I-\mu A_n)^{-1}$ converges uniformly to $(I-\mu A)^{-1}$ in the subspace H_z. Consider the relation

$$(I-\mu A_n)^{-1}-(I-\mu A)^{-1} = \{[I-\mu(I-\mu A)^{-1}(A_n-A)]^{-1}-I\}(I-\mu A)^{-1}$$

$$= \sum_{k=1}^{\infty} \mu^k [(I-\mu A)^{-1}(A_n-A)]^k (I-\mu A)^{-1}.$$

Then

$$\|(I-\mu A_n)^{-1}-(I-\mu A)^{-1}\|$$

$$\leq \|(I-\mu A)^{-1}\| \sum_{k=1}^{\infty} |\mu|^k \|(I-\mu A)^{-1}\|^k \|A_n-A\|^k$$

$$= \frac{|\mu|\|(I-\mu A)^{-1}\|^2}{1-|\mu|\|(I-\mu A)^{-1}\|\|A-A_n\|} \|A-A_n\| \to 0,$$

since $\|A-A_n\|$ approaches zero in H_z when $n \to \infty$. But f clearly belongs to H_z, and therefore the sequence $x_n = (I-\mu A_n)^{-1}f$ converges (strongly) to $x = (I-\mu A)^{-1}f$. The proof of the theorem is complete.

By means of formula (20), Chapter I, it is possible to estimate the accuracy achieved. In the present case, $F_{n-1}(\lambda) \equiv 1$ and

$$x_n = (I-\mu A_n)^{-1}\left[I-\frac{1}{P_n\left(\frac{1}{\mu}\right)}P_n(A_n)\right]f. \tag{5}$$

On the other hand, $x_n = Q_{n-1}(A_n)f$ is an $(n-1)$st degree polynomial in A_n, while from the definition of A_n, $A^k f = A_n^k f$ $(k=0,1,\ldots,n-1)$. Therefore, $x_n = Q_{n-1}(A_n)f = Q_{n-1}(A)f$,

$$x_n = (I-\mu A)^{-1}\left[I-\frac{1}{P_n\left(\frac{1}{\mu}\right)}P_n(A)\right]f,$$

and

$$x-x_n = (I-\mu A)^{-1}\frac{P_n(A)f}{P_n\left(\frac{1}{\mu}\right)}.$$

Thus, the following error estimate holds:

$$\|x-x_n\| \leq \|(I-\mu A)^{-1}\|\frac{\|P_n(A)f\|}{\left|P_n\left(\frac{1}{\mu}\right)\right|}. \tag{6}$$

We might note that when solving equation (1) by the method of moments, one is not at all obliged to take the initial element z_0 to be f. Any element may be chosen as z_0. The only restriction is that f belong to the subspace H_z.

Replacing equation (1) by the approximate equation

$$x_n = \mu A_n x_n + f_n,$$

with f_n the projection of f on H_n, we can find x_n by applying the formulas of Chapter I.

The actual calculation of the approximations x_n may prove difficult for large n. This is mainly connected with the fact that to obtain the coefficients of $P_n(\lambda)$, one has to solve the system of linear equations (11), Chapter I. As n increases, the number of equations of course increases and the determinant of the system, especially in the case of a completely continuous operator, decreases fairly rapidly resulting in a progressive loss in computational accuracy. It may thus prove more reasonable to avoid using the moments method to compute an approximate solution and instead to use it to accelerate the convergence of some iterative process.

In the classical Liouville-Neumann method, successive approximations are constructed according to the formula

$$x_{n+1} = \mu A x_n + f, \quad x_0 = f,$$

or

$$x_n = f + \mu A f + \ldots + \mu^n A^n f.$$

The successive approximations converge to the solution in the region

$$|\mu| < \frac{1}{\|A\|},$$

but the speed of convergence is slow if $|\mu|$ is close to $\|A\|^{-1}$.

By use of the method of moments, this process may be so transformed that the new process will converge for each regular value of μ at a rate subject to our control.

On the basis of the sequence of iterations

$$z_0 = f, \quad z_1 = Af, \ldots, z_n = A^n,$$

and with n fixed, we construct the operator A_n.

We then express equation (1) in the form

$$x - \mu A_n x + \mu(A_n - A)x = f.$$

The operator $(I - \mu A_n)^{-1}$ exists when n is sufficiently great. Hence, applying it to both sides of the last equation, we obtain

$$x = \mu(I - \mu A_n)^{-1}(A - A_n)x + (I - \mu A_n)^{-1}f. \tag{1'}$$

We solve this equation by the Liouville-Neumann method and to this end, we define $x^{(0)} = (I - \mu A_n)^{-1}f$ and successive approximations by the formula

$$x^{(k+1)} = \mu(I - \mu A_n)^{-1}(A - A_n)x^{(k)} + (I - \mu A_n)^{-1}f. \tag{7}$$

To compute $x^{(k+1)}$ from $x^{(k)}$, we must solve the equation

$$x^{(k+1)} - \mu A_n x^{(k+1)} = \mu(A - A_n)x^{(k)} + f. \tag{8}$$

We start by applying to both sides of this equation the operator projecting onto the subspace H_n. Making use of the fact that $E_n f = f$ and $E_n A_n = E_n^2 A E_n = A_n = E_n A E_n^2 = A_n E_n$ (recall that $E_n^2 = E_n$), we have

$$E_n x^{(k+1)} - \mu A_n E_n x^{(k+1)} = \mu(E_n A - A_n)x^{(k)} + f. \tag{9}$$

The solution $E_n x^{(k+1)}$ of this equation, which we denote by $x_n^{(k+1)}$, may be found by means of equations (20), (20'), (21), Chapter I. Next, subtracting (9) from (8), we obtain

$$x^{(k+1)} - x_n^{(k+1)} = \mu(A - E_n A)x^{(k)},$$

or

$$x^{(k+1)} = x_n^{(k+1)} + \mu(A - E_n A)x^{(k)}. \tag{10}$$

Let us assume that $x^{(k)}$ has the form

$$x^{(k)} = \sum_{j=0}^{n+k-1} d_j^{(k)} z_j,$$

and let us compute $(A - A_n)x^{(k)}$. We find that

$$(A - A_n)x^{(k)} = (A - E_n A E_n)x^{(k)} = \sum_{j=0}^{n+k-1} d_j^{(k)} z_{j+1}$$

$$- \sum_{j=0}^{n-2} d_j^{(k)} z_{j+1} - \sum_{j=n-1}^{n+k-1} d_j^{(k)} E_n A E_n z_j$$

$$= \sum_{j=n-1}^{n+k-1} d_j^{(k)} (z_{j+1} - E_n A E_n z_j).$$

Now let

$$E_n z_j = \sum_{s=0}^{n-1} l_s^{(j)} z_s,$$

the $l_s^{(j)}$ being determined from the system of equations

$$(z_p, z_0)l_0^{(j)} + (z_p, z_1)l_1^{(j)} + \ldots + (z_p, z_{n-1})l_{n-1}^{(j)} = (z_p, z_j)$$

$$(p = 0, 1, \ldots, n-1).$$

Then
$$AE_n z_j = \sum_{s=0}^{n-1} l_s^{(j)} z_{s+1},$$

and

$$E_n AE_n z_j = \sum_{s=0}^{n-2} l_s^{(j)} z_{s+1} + l_{n-1}^{(j)} E_n z_n = \sum_{s=1}^{n-1} l_{s-1}^{(j)} z_s - l_{n-1}^{(j)} \sum_{s=0}^{n-1} \alpha_s z_s$$

$$= \sum_{s=0}^{n-1} (l_{s-1}^{(j)} - l_{n-1}^{(j)} \alpha_s) z_s \quad (l_{-1}^{(j)} = 0). \tag{11}$$

Thus

$$(A - A_n)x^{(k)} = \sum_{j=n-1}^{n+k-1} d_j^{(k)} \left[z_{j+1} - \sum_{s=0}^{n-1} (l_{s-1}^{(j)} - l_{n-1}^{(j)} \alpha_s) z_s \right]$$

$$= \sum_{j=n-1}^{n+k-1} d_j^{(k)} (z_{j+1} - E_n z_{j+1})$$

$$+ \sum_{j=n-1}^{n+k-1} d_j^{(k)} \left[\sum_{s=0}^{n-1} (l_s^{(j+1)} - l_{s-1}^{(j)} + l_{n-1}^{(j)} \alpha_s) z_s \right].$$

The application of E_n to both sides of this equation yields

$$(E_n A - A_n)x^{(k)} = \sum_{j=n-1}^{n+k-1} d_j^{(k)} \left[\sum_{s=0}^{n-1} (l_s^{(j+1)} - l_{s-1}^{(j)} + l_{n-1}^{(j)} \alpha_s) z_s \right]$$

$$= \sum_{s=0}^{n-1} z_s \left[\sum_{j=n-1}^{n+k-1} d_j^{(k)} (l_s^{(j+1)} - l_{s-1}^{(j)} + l_{n-1}^{(j)} \alpha_s) \right]$$

and subtraction from the old equation leads to

$$(A - E_n A)x^{(k)} = \sum_{j=n-1}^{n+k-1} d_j^{(k)} (z_{j+1} - E_n z_{j+1})$$

$$= \sum_{j=n-1}^{n+k-1} d_j^{(k)} \left(z_{j+1} - \sum_{s=0}^{n-1} l_s^{(j+1)} z_s \right) = \sum_{s=0}^{n+k} h_s^{(k+1)} z_s,$$

where

$$h_s^{(k+1)} = - \sum_{j=n-1}^{n+k-1} l_s^{(j+1)} d_j^{(k)} \quad (s = 0, 1, \ldots, n-1),$$

$$h_s^{(k+1)} = d_{s-1}^{(k)} \quad (s = n, \ldots, n+k).$$

It still remains to solve the equation [Cf. (9)]

$$x_n^{(k+1)} - \mu A_n x_n^{(k+1)} = \mu(E_n A - A_n)x^{(k)} + f. \tag{12}$$

Putting

$$x_n^{(k+1)} = x_0 + \mu \sum_{s=0}^{n-1} a_s^{(k+1)} z_s,$$

we can find the coefficients $a_s^{(k+1)}$ using the formulas (21) of Chapter I, to wit,

$$a_0^{(k+1)} = \sum_{j=n-1}^{n+k-1} d_j^{(k)}(l_0^{(j+1)} + l_{n-1}^{(j)}\alpha_0) - \frac{F_{n-1}^{(k+1)}\left(\dfrac{1}{\mu}\right)}{P_n\left(\dfrac{1}{\mu}\right)}\alpha_0,$$

$$a_s^{(k+1)} = \sum_{j=n-1}^{n+k-1} d_j^{(k)}(l_s^{(j+1)} - l_{s-1}^{(j)} + l_{n-1}^{(j)}\alpha_s)$$

$$+ \mu a_{s-1}^{(k+1)} - \frac{F_{n-1}^{(k+1)}\left(\dfrac{1}{\mu}\right)}{P_n\left(\dfrac{1}{\mu}\right)}\alpha_s \quad (s = 1, 2, \ldots, n-1),$$

where $\quad F_{n-1}^{(k+1)}(\lambda) = \displaystyle\sum_{s=0}^{n-1}\left[\sum_{j=n-1}^{n+k-1} d_j^{(k)}(l_s^{(j+1)} - l_{s-1}^{(j)} + \alpha_s l_{n-1}^{(j)})\right]\lambda^s.$

Thus, from (10), we finally conclude that

$$x^{(k+1)} = \sum_{s=0}^{n+k} d_s^{(k+1)} z_s,$$

with $\quad d_s^{(k+1)} = \mu h_s^{(k+1)} + d_s^{(0)} + \mu a_s^{(k+1)} \quad (s = 0, 1, \ldots, n-1),$

$$d_s^{(k+1)} = \mu h_s^{(k+1)} \quad\quad\quad (s = n, \ldots, n+k).$$

The first approximation has an especially simple form. Setting $k = 0$ and using the fact that

$$l_s^{(n)} = -\alpha_s, \quad l_s^{(j)} = \begin{cases} 0 & j \neq s \\ 1 & j = s \end{cases} \quad (j < n),$$

we obtain $\quad h_s^{(1)} = -l_s^{(n)} d_{n-1}^{(0)} = \alpha_s d_{n-1}^{(0)} \quad (s = 0, 1, \ldots, n-1),$

$$h_n^{(1)} = d_{n-1}^{(0)}.$$

Next, since $\quad l_s^{(n)} - l_{s-1}^{(n-1)} + l_{n-1}^{(n-1)}\alpha_s = -\alpha_s + \alpha_s = 0,$

$F_{n-1}^{(1)}(\lambda) \equiv 0$ and therefore, $x_n^{(1)} = x^{(0)}$. Hence,

$$x^{(1)} = \sum_{s=0}^{n} d_s^{(1)} z_s,$$

where

$$d_s^{(1)} = \mu \alpha_s d_{n-1}^{(0)} - d_s^{(0)},$$

$$d_n^{(1)} = \mu d_{n-1}^{(0)}.$$

Let us study the speed of convergence of the process. To this end, we consider the basic formula

$$x^{(k+1)} = \mu(I - \mu A_n)^{-1}(A - A_n)x^{(k)} + (I - \mu A_n)^{-1}f. \tag{7}$$

For brevity, we express it as

$$x^{(k+1)} = Bx^{(k)} + x^{(0)}, \tag{7'}$$

with $x^{(0)} = (I - \mu A_n)^{-1}f$ and $B = \mu(I - \mu A_n)^{-1}(A - A_n)$. Since the operators $(I - \mu A_n)^{-1}$ are uniformly bounded for sufficiently large n and since $\|A - A_n\| \to 0$, given any arbitrarily small positive quantity q we can find an n such that

$$\|B\| \leq |\mu| \, \|(I - \mu A_n)^{-1}\| \, \|A - A_n\| < q.$$

Choose such a value of n and fix it.

From (7'), it follows that

$$x^{(k)} = \sum_{j=0}^{k} B^j x^{(0)}.$$

If x denotes the desired solution of (1'), then according to Banach's Theorem, we have

$$x_* = \sum_{j=0}^{\infty} B^j x^{(0)}.$$

Subtraction then yields

$$\|x_* - x^{(k)}\| = \left\| B^{k+1} \sum_{j=0}^{\infty} B^j x^{(0)} \right\| \leq \|B\|^{k+1} \|x_*\|,$$

or

$$\|x_* - x^{(k)}\| \leq q^{k+1} \|x_*\|. \tag{13}$$

Thus, the process converges no slower than a geometric progression with ratio q, which can be made arbitrarily small by increasing n.

Since $x^{(k)}$ is a polynomial in A of the form

$$x^{(k)} = G_{n+k-1}(A)f,$$

we have simultaneously proved the following

Lemma: *If x_* is a solution of*

$$x = \mu Ax + f, \tag{1}$$

with μ a regular value and A a completely continuous operator, then for any arbitrarily small positive quantity q, there exists a polynomial $G_{m-1}(\lambda)$ and a number C not depending on m such that

$$\| x_* - G_{m-1}(A)f \| \leq Cq^m.$$

For, consider $G_{m-1}(A)f = x^{(m-n)}$. The inequality (13) implies that

$$\| x_* - G_{m-1}(A)f \| = \| x_* - x^{(m-n)} \| \leq q^{m-n+1} \cdot \| x_* \| = Cq^m,$$

where $C = \| x_* \| q^{1-n}$ is independent of m.

On the basis of this lemma, we can prove a theorem which provides some idea of the speed of convergence of the approximations in the method of moments.

Theorem VII: *If μ is a regular value for the equation*

$$x = \mu Ax + f \tag{1}$$

in which A is a completely continuous operator, then the sequence x_m of solutions of

$$x_m = \mu A_m x_m + f$$

converges to the solution x_* of equation (1) faster than a geometric progression with any arbitrarily small ratio $q > 0$.

Proof: Let y_m denote the polynomial $G_{m-1}(A)f$ figuring in the lemma. Then

$$y_m - \mu A_m y_m = E_m y_m - \mu E_m A E_m y_m = E_m(y_m - \mu A y_m),$$

since y_m belongs to the subspace H_m.

Next,

$$x_m - \mu A_m x_m = f = x_* - \mu A x_* = E_m(x_* - \mu A x_*).$$

Subtracting the last two equations, we obtain

$$x_m - y_m - \mu A_m(x_m - y_m) = E_m[x_* - y_m - \mu A(x_* - y_m)],$$

or $$x_m - y_m = (I - \mu A_m)^{-1} E_m[x_* - y_m - \mu A(x_* - y_m)].$$

Hence, by the lemma

$$\| x_m - y_m \| \leq \| (I - \mu A_m)^{-1} \| \, \| I - \mu A \| \, \| x_* - y_m \|$$

$$\leq \| (I - \mu A_m)^{-1} \| \, \| I - \mu A \| \, Cq^m.$$

The application of the triangle inequality then yields

$$\| x_* - x_m \| \leq \| x_* - y_m \| + \| y_m - x_m \|$$
$$\leq C[1 + \| (I - \mu A_m)^{-1} \| \, \| I - \mu A \|] q^m.$$

Since the operators $(I - \mu A_m)^{-1}$ are uniformly bounded for sufficiently large m, there exists a constant D independent of m such that

$$C(1 + \| (I - \mu A_m)^{-1} \| \, \| I - \mu A \|) \leq D.$$

Thus, $$\| x_* - x_m \| \leq D q^m,$$

where q is any arbitrarily small positive quantity. The theorem is proved.

3. Homogeneous Equations. Determination of Eigenvalues

We now proceed to the solution of homogeneous equations involving completely continuous operators.

Theorem VIII: *If A is a completely continuous operator and μ one of its reciprocal eigenvalues, that is, the equation*

$$u - \mu A u = 0 \tag{14}$$

has a non-trivial solution in H_z, then each such solution is unique to within a factor, or in other words, to each eigenvalue there corresponds but one eigenelement in H_z. As n increases, one of the solutions of

$$u_n - \mu_n A_n u_n = 0 \tag{15}$$

tends to the solution of (14) *faster than a geometric progression with any arbitrarily small ratio $q > 0$.*

Proof: We first express (14) in the form

$$u - \mu A u = u - \mu(A - A_n)u - \mu A_n u = 0. \tag{15'}$$

By Banach's Theorem, all values of μ in the circular region

$$|\mu| < \frac{1}{\| A - A_n \|}, \tag{16}$$

are regular for the operator $I - \mu(A - A_n)$ or, in other words, the inverse operator $[I - \mu(A - A_n)]^{-1}$ exists. The fulfillment of condition (16) can always be assured since with increasing n, $\| A - A_n \| \to 0$ by Theorem IV.

Equation (14) may be expressed in the form

$$u - \mu Au = [I - \mu(A - A_n)]\{I - \mu[I - \mu(A - A_n)]^{-1}A_n\}u = 0.$$

On applying $[I - \mu(A - A_n)]^{-1}$ to both sides, we conclude that

$$u = \mu[I - \mu(A - A_n)]^{-1}A_n u. \tag{17}$$

Now $A_n u \in H_n$ and hence is representable as

$$A_n u = \sum_{k=0}^{n-1} \frac{b_k}{\mu} z_k,$$

with certain constant coefficients b_k. Introducing the notation

$$\xi_k = [I - \mu(A - A_n)]^{-1} z_k, \tag{18}$$

we obtain from (17) the following expression for u:

$$u = \sum_{k=0}^{n-1} b_k \xi_k. \tag{19}$$

The elements ξ_k are linearly independent. For, if to the contrary there existed numbers C_k not all vanishing such that

$$\sum_{k=0}^{n-1} C_k \xi_k = 0,$$

then $$\sum_{k=0}^{n-1} C_k \xi_k = [I - \mu(A - A_n)]^{-1} \sum_{k=0}^{n-1} C_k z_k = 0.$$

Hence, the last sum would have to vanish which would contradict the linear independence of the z_k.

The equation defining ξ_k is equivalent to

$$\xi_k - \mu(A - A_n)\xi_k = z_k,$$

and the formulas (22) of Chapter I therefore imply that

$$\xi_k = z_k \quad (k = 0, 1, \dots, n-2).$$

Thus, $$A_n u = \sum_{k=0}^{n-2} b_k z_{k+1} + b_{n-1} A_n \xi_{n-1},$$

$$[I - \mu(A - A_n)]^{-1}A_n u = \sum_{k=0}^{n-2} b_k \xi_{k+1} + b_{n-1}[I - \mu(A - A_n)]^{-1}A_n \xi_{n-1}.$$

$$\tag{20}$$

Since $A_n \xi_{n-1}$ is in H_n, there exist numbers $\alpha_s(\mu)$ such that

$$A_n \xi_{n-1} = -\sum_{s=0}^{n-1} \alpha_s(\mu) z_s$$

and so
$$[I - \mu(A - A_n)]^{-1} A_n \xi_{n-1} = -\sum_{s=0}^{n-1} \alpha_s(\mu) \xi_s. \tag{21}$$

The substitution of (19), (20), and (21) into (17) next leads to

$$\sum_{k=0}^{n-1} [b_k - \mu b_{k-1} + \mu \alpha_k(\mu) b_{n-1}] \xi_k = 0, \quad b_{-1} = 0.$$

Hence, in view of the linear independence of the ξ_k, their coefficients must vanish. This yields

$$b_k - \mu b_{k-1} + \mu \alpha_k(\mu) b_{n-1} = 0 \quad (k = 0, 1, \ldots, n-1). \tag{22}$$

Equating to zero the determinant of this system of homogeneous linear equations, we arrive at the following equation for the reciprocal eigenvalues μ:

$$\Delta(\mu) = \frac{1}{\mu^n} + \frac{\alpha_{n-1}(\mu)}{\mu^{n-1}} + \ldots + \frac{\alpha_1(\mu)}{\mu} + \alpha_0(\mu) = 0. \tag{23}$$

After having found an eigenvalue, we obtain a corresponding eigenelement from (19), the coefficients b_k being calculated by use of the recursion formulas

$$b_k = \mu[b_{k-1} - \alpha_k(\mu)] \quad (k = 0, 1, \ldots, n-2), \quad b_{n-1} = 1. \tag{22'}$$

But since the b_k are uniquely determined, it follows that to each reciprocal eigenvalue there corresponds but one eigenelement determined of course to within a numerical factor.

We now prove the second part of the theorem. We first observe that for sufficiently large m $(m > n)$, the equation

$$u_m - \mu A_m u_m = 0$$

can be transformed as before into

$$u_m = \mu[I - \mu(A_m - A_n)]^{-1} A_n u. \tag{17'}$$

Letting $\xi_k^{(m)} = [I - \mu(A_m - A_n)]^{-1} z_k$, we look for a solution u_m of the form

$$u_m = \sum_{k=0}^{n-1} b_k^{(m)} \xi_k^{(m)}, \quad \xi_k^{(m)} = z_k \quad (k = 0, 1, \ldots, n-2).$$

Repeating the reasoning used to determine the reciprocal eigenvalues and eigenelements of the operator A, we arrive at a system of equations similar to (22)

$$b_k^{(m)} - \mu b_{k-1}^{(m)} + \mu \alpha_k^{(m)}(\mu) b_{n-1}^{(m)} = 0 \quad (k = 0, 1, \ldots, n-1), \tag{22''}$$

the quantities $\alpha_k^{(m)}(\mu)$ being defined by the relation

$$A_n \zeta_{n-1}^{(m)} = -\sum_{s=0}^{n-1} \alpha_s^{(m)}(\mu) z_s.$$

Since ξ_{n-1} and $\zeta_{n-1}^{(m)}$ are respective solutions of

$$\xi_{n-1} - \mu(A - A_n)\xi_{n-1} = z_{n-1},$$

$$\zeta_{n-1}^{(m)} - \mu(A_m - A_n)\zeta_{n-1}^{(m)} = z_{n-1}$$

and since the sequence A_m converges in norm to A, according to the lemma of §2, there exists a polynomial $\tilde{Q}_s(A - A_n)z_{n-1}$ such that

$$\| \xi_{n-1} - \tilde{Q}_s(A - A_n)z_{n-1} \| \leq Cq^s,$$

with q some positive number. But $\tilde{Q}_s(A - A_n)z_{n-1} = Q_{s+n-1}(A)z_0$, so that for $m = n+s$,

$$\| \xi_{n-1} - Q_{m-1}(A)z_0 \| \leq Cq^{m-n} = C_1 q^m.$$

Now let $y_{n-1}^{(m)} = Q_{m-1}(A)z_0$. Then

$$y_{n-1}^{(m)} - \mu(A_m - A_n)y_{n-1}^{(m)} = E_m[y_{n-1}^{(m)} - \mu(A - A_n)y_{n-1}^{(m)}]$$

and $\zeta_{n-1}^{(m)} - \mu(A_m - A_n)\zeta_{n-1}^{(m)} = z_{n-1} = E_n[\xi_{n-1} - \mu(A - A_n)\xi_{n-1}].$

The subtraction of the last two relations gives

$$\zeta_{n-1}^{(m)} - y_{n-1}^{(m)} - \mu(A_m - A_n)(\zeta_{n-1}^{(m)} - y_{n-1}^{(m)})$$

$$= E_n[\xi_{n-1} - y_{n-1}^{(m)} - \mu(A - A_n)(\xi_{n-1} - y_{n-1}^{(m)})].$$

Hence,

$$\| \zeta_{n-1}^{(m)} - y_{n-1}^{(m)} \| \leq \| [I - \mu(A_m - A_n)]^{-1} \|$$

$$\times \| I - \mu(A - A_n) \| \, \| \xi_{n-1} - y_{n-1}^{(m)} \|.$$

Thus, there exists a constant C_2 such that

$$\| \zeta_{n-1}^{(m)} - y_{n-1}^{(m)} \| \leq C_2 q^m.$$

Applying the triangle inequality, we finally obtain

$$\| \xi_{n-1} - \zeta_{n-1}^{(m)} \| \leq C_3 q^m.$$

From the way in which $\alpha_s(\mu)$ and $\alpha_s^{(m)}(\mu)$ are defined, it follows that a similar kind of estimate holds for them, namely,

$$|\alpha_s(\mu) - \alpha_s^{(m)}(\mu)| \leq C^{(s)} \cdot q^m,$$

where $C^{(s)}$ is a constant independent of m.

Now let $\Delta_m(\mu)$ denote the characteristic polynomial for the operator A_m:

$$\Delta_m(\mu) = \frac{1}{\mu^n} + \frac{\alpha_{n-1}^{(m)}(\mu)}{\mu^{n-1}} + \ldots + \alpha_0^{(m)}(\mu).$$

From the estimate for $\alpha_s(\mu)$, it then follows that

$$|\Delta(\mu) - \Delta_m(\mu)| \leq C'q^m.$$

Suppose that μ_0 is a root of the equation $\Delta(\mu) = 0$ of multiplicity ρ satisfying condition (16). Then for sufficiently small $r = |\mu - \mu_0|$,

$$|\Delta(\mu)| \geq C''r^\rho.$$

For $r = (C'/C'')^{1/\rho} q^{m/\rho}$, we further have

$$|\Delta(\mu) - \Delta_m(\mu)| \leq C''r^\rho \leq |\Delta(\mu)|.$$

Therefore, by Rouché's Theorem, $\Delta_m(\mu) = \Delta(\mu) + \Delta_m(\mu) - \Delta(\mu)$ has exactly ρ roots $\mu_m^{(1)}, \ldots, \mu_m^{(\rho)}$ in the region $|\mu - \mu_0| \leq r$ which satisfy the inequalities

$$|\mu_0 - \mu_m^{(k)}| \leq \bar{C}\bar{q}^m \quad (k = 1, \ldots, \rho),$$

where
$$\bar{C} = \left(\frac{C'}{C''}\right)^{1/\rho}, \quad \bar{q} = q^{1/\rho}.$$

Hence, in view of the arbitrariness of q, the eigenvalues of the "approximate" equation (15) converge to the eigenvalues of equation (14) (provided they exist) faster than any geometric progression having an arbitrarily small positive ratio. The estimate for the eigenvalues and the equations (22), (22'), and (22'') in turn imply the same sort of convergence for the eigenelements. The proof of the theorem is complete.

The determination of the reciprocal eigenvalues μ_n and eigenelements u_n may be effected by the method presented in §3, Chapter I. It is only necessary to remember that the reciprocal eigenvalues and eigenvalues of A_n are reciprocally related:

$$\mu_n = \frac{1}{\lambda_n}.$$

As already mentioned above, the actual computation of the co-efficients of the polynomial $P_n(\lambda)$ and, therefore the determination of the eigenvalues of A_n may be difficult for large values of n and may involve considerable loss of computational accuracy. In such a case, the method of Schmidt used in the proof of Theorem VI will be of help. By means of it, several of the eigenvalues that are largest in absolute value as well as their corresponding eigenelements may be computed without having to increase n.

Keeping n fixed, we now show how power series may be obtained for the coefficients $\alpha_k(\mu)$ in equations (22) and (23) determining the reciprocal eigenvalues and eigenelements.

The coefficients $\alpha_s(\mu)$ were defined by the relation

$$A_n \xi_{n-1} = -\sum_{s=0}^{n-1} \alpha_s(\mu) z_s,$$

in which $\xi_{n-1} = [I - \mu(A - A_n)]^{-1} z_{n-1} = \sum_{j=0}^{\infty} \mu^j (A - A_n)^j z_{n-1}.$

We first derive recursion formulas for the coefficients of the latter power series. Let

$$(A - A_n)^j z_{n-1} = \sum_{s=0}^{n+j-1} d_s^{(j)} z_s.$$

Then

$$(A - A_n)^{j+1} z_{n-1} = \sum_{s=0}^{n+j-1} d_s^{(j)} z_{s+1}$$

$$- \sum_{s=0}^{n+j-1} d_s^{(j)} A_n z_s = \sum_{s=n-1}^{n+j-1} d_s^{(j)} z_{s+1} - \sum_{s=n-1}^{n+j-1} d_s^{(j)} A_n z_s.$$

From (11), we have

$$A_n z_s = \sum_{k=0}^{n-1} (l_{k-1}^{(s)} - l_{n-1}^{(s)} \alpha_k) z_k,$$

so that

$$(A - A_n)^{j+1} z_{n-1} = \sum_{s=0}^{n+j} d_s^{(j+1)} z_s$$

$$= \sum_{s=n-1}^{n+j-1} d_s^{(j)} z_{s+1} - \sum_{k=0}^{n-1} z_k \left[\sum_{s=n-1}^{n+j-1} d_s^{(j)} (l_{k-1}^{(s)} - l_{n-1}^{(s)} \alpha_k) \right].$$

Thus,

$$\left. \begin{aligned} d_s^{(j+1)} &= d_{s-1}^{(j)} \quad (s = n, \ldots, n+j), \\ d_s^{(j+1)} &= -\sum_{k=n-1}^{n+j-1} d_k^{(j)} (l_{s-1}^{(k)} - l_{n-1}^{(k)} \alpha_s) \quad (s = 0, 1, \ldots, n-1) \end{aligned} \right\} \tag{24}$$

and $\xi_{n-1} = \sum_{j=0}^{\infty} \mu^j (A - A_n)^j z_{n-1} = \sum_{j=0}^{\infty} \mu^j \sum_{s=0}^{n+j-1} d_s^{(j)} z_s.$

We next compute $A_n \xi_{n-1}$ as follows:

$$A_n \xi_{n-1} = \sum_{j=0}^{\infty} \mu^j \left[\sum_{s=0}^{n+j-1} d_s^{(j)} A_n z_s \right]$$

$$= \sum_{j=0}^{\infty} \left[\sum_{s=0}^{n+j-1} d_s^{(j)} \sum_{k=0}^{n-1} (l_{k-1}^{(s)} - l_{n-1}^{(s)} \alpha_k) z_k \right] \mu^j.$$

An interchange in the order of summation yields

$$A_n \xi_{n-1} = \sum_{k=0}^{n-1} z_k \left\{ \sum_{j=0}^{\infty} \mu^j \left[\sum_{s=0}^{n+j-1} d_s^{(j)} (l_{k-1}^{(s)} - l_{n-1}^{(s)} \alpha_k) \right] \right\}$$

$$= - \sum_{k=0}^{n-1} \alpha_k(\mu) z_k,$$

from which we finally obtain the required series

$$\alpha_k(\mu) = - \sum_{j=0}^{\infty} \left[\sum_{s=0}^{n+j-1} d_s^{(j)} (l_{k-1}^{(s)} - l_{n-1}^{(s)} \alpha_k) \right] \mu^j. \qquad (25)$$

The series is absolutely convergent in the region

$$|\mu| < \frac{1}{\| A - A_n \|}.$$

Let us compute the first two terms of the series. We have

$$\alpha_k(\mu) = - \sum_{s=0}^{n-1} d_s^{(0)} (l_{k-1}^{(s)} - l_{n-1}^{(s)} \alpha_k) - \mu \sum_{s=0}^{n} d_s^{(1)} (l_{k-1}^{(s)} - l_{n-1}^{(s)} \alpha_k) - \ldots$$

$$\xi_k = z_k \quad (k = 0, 1, \ldots, n-2),$$

$$\xi_{n-1} = z_{n-1} + \mu(A - A_n) z_{n-1} + \ldots = z_{n-1} + \mu \sum_{s=0}^{n} d_s^{(1)} z_s + \ldots$$

Since
$$z_{n-1} = \sum_{s=0}^{n-1} d_s^{(0)} z_s,$$

it follows that $d_s^{(0)} = 0$ $(s = 0, 1, \ldots, n-2)$, $d_{n-1}^{(0)} = 1$.

If we take into consideration that

$$l_s^{(n)} = -\alpha_s, \quad l_s^{(j)} = \begin{cases} 0 & j \neq s \\ 1 & j = s \end{cases} \quad (j < n),$$

using the recursion formulas (24) we conclude that

$$d_n^{(1)} = d_{n-1}^{(0)} = 1,$$

$$d_s^{(1)} = -d_{n-1}^{(0)}(l_{s-1}^{(n-1)} - l_{n-1}^{(n-1)}\alpha_s) = \alpha_s \quad (s = 0, 1, \ldots, n-1).$$

Thus, $\xi_{n-1} = z_{n-1} + \mu \sum_{s=0}^{n} \alpha_s z_s + \ldots = z_{n-1} + \mu P_n(A)z_0 + \ldots$

Finally, we compute $\alpha_k(\mu)$:

$$-\sum_{s=0}^{n-1} d_s^{(0)}(l_{k-1}^{(s)} - l_{n-1}^{(s)}\alpha_k)$$

$$= -(l_{k-1}^{(n-1)} - l_{n-1}^{(n-1)}\alpha_k) = \alpha_k \quad (k = 0, 1, \ldots, n-1),$$

$$\sum_{s=0}^{n} d_s^{(1)}(l_{k-1}^{(s)} - l_{n-1}^{(s)}\alpha_k) = d_{k-1}^{(1)} - d_{n-1}^{(1)}\alpha_k + d_n^{(1)}(-\alpha_{k-1} + \alpha_{n-1}\alpha_k)$$

$$= \alpha_{k-1}\alpha_{n-1}\alpha_k - \alpha_{k-1} + \alpha_{n-1}\alpha_k = 0.$$

Therefore, the coefficient of the first-degree term in the power series (25) vanishes and to terms of second order in μ, we have

$$\alpha_k(\mu) = \alpha_k.$$

Hence, the eigenvalues can be found from the equation

$$\Delta_n(\mu) = P_n\left(\frac{1}{\mu}\right) = 0.$$

They obviously coincide with the eigenvalues of the operator A_n.

After (22') is used to compute b_k recursively, each of the eigen-elements can be found from

$$u = \sum_{k=0}^{n-1} b_k \xi_k = \sum_{k=0}^{n-1} b_k z_k + b_{n-1}\mu P_n(A)z_0. \tag{26}$$

4. Example of Eigenvalue Calculation

A problem arising in heat conduction requires the solution of the equation

$$-y''(x) = \mu y(x) \tag{27}$$

under the boundary conditions

$$y(0) = 0, \quad y(1) + y'(1) = 0. \tag{28}$$

By means of Green's function, equation (27) is easily converted into an integral equation

$$y = \mu \int_0^1 K(x, \xi) y(\xi) \, d\xi, \tag{29}$$

where

$$K(x, \xi) = \begin{cases} \frac{1}{2}(2-\xi)x & x \leqq \xi, \\ \frac{1}{2}(2-x)\xi & x \geqq \xi. \end{cases}$$

The operator

$$Ay = \int_0^1 K(x, \xi) y(\xi) \, d\xi$$

is completely continuous in L_2 space, the interval of integration being $[0, 1]$.

For the function z_0, we choose

$$z_0(x) = \sin \pi x.$$

The sequence z_k may be found either by successive integration:

$$z_{k+1}(x) = \int_0^1 K(x, \xi) z_k(\xi) \, d\xi,$$

or by solving the recursive equations

$$-z_{k+1}''(x) = z_k(x)$$

under the boundary conditions $z_{k+1}(0) = 0$, $z_{k+1}'(1) + z_{k+1}(1) = 0$. The latter procedure is slightly simpler requiring no knowledge of Green's function.

Performing the first few quadratures, we obtain

$$z_1(x) = \frac{x}{2\pi} + \frac{1}{\pi^2} \sin \pi x,$$

$$z_2(x) = \frac{x}{6\pi} \left(1 + \frac{3}{\pi^2} \right) - \frac{x^3}{12\pi} + \frac{1}{\pi^4} \sin \pi x,$$

$$z_3(x) = \left(\frac{31}{720\pi} + \frac{1}{6\pi^3} + \frac{1}{2\pi^5} \right) x - \frac{x^3}{36\pi} \left(1 + \frac{3}{\pi^2} \right) + \frac{x^5}{240\pi} + \frac{\sin \pi x}{\pi^6}.$$

We next compute the scalar products needed in the system (11) of Chapter I:

$$(z_0, z_0) = \int_0^1 z_0^2(x)\, dx = 0.5,$$

$$(z_0, z_1) = \int_0^1 z_0(x)z_1(x)\, dx = 0.1013212,$$

$$(z_0, z_2) = (z_1, z_1) = 10^{-2} \cdot 2.384240,$$

$$(z_0, z_3) = (z_1, z_2) = 10^{-3} \cdot 5.761453,$$

$$(z_1, z_3) = (z_2, z_2) = 10^{-3} \cdot 1.398529,$$

$$(z_2, z_3) = 10^{-4} \cdot 3.397373.$$

Thus, the coefficients in the characteristic equation for the first three approximations are found to satisfy the following three systems of equations:

$n = 1$ $0.5\alpha_0 + 0.1013212 = 0;$

$n = 2$ $\left.\begin{array}{l} 0.5000000\alpha_0 + 0.1013212\alpha_1 + 10^{-2} \cdot 2.384240 = 0, \\ 0.1013212\alpha_0 + 10^{-2} \cdot 2.384240\alpha_1 + 10^{-3} \cdot 5.761453 = 0; \end{array}\right\}$

$n = 3$ $\left.\begin{array}{l} 0.5000000\alpha_0 + 0.1013212\alpha_1 \\ \qquad + 10^{-2} \cdot 2.384240\alpha_2 + 10^{-3} \cdot 5.761453 = 0, \\[4pt] 0.1013212\alpha_0 + 10^{-2} \cdot 2.384240\alpha_1 \\ \qquad + 10^{-3} \cdot 5.761453\alpha_2 + 10^{-3} \cdot 1.398529 = 0, \\[4pt] 10^{-2} \cdot 2.384240\alpha_0 + 10^{-3} \cdot 5.761453\alpha_1 \\ \qquad + 10^{-3} \cdot 1.398529\alpha_2 + 10^{-4} \cdot 3.397373 = 0. \end{array}\right\}$

Their respective solutions are

$$n = 1 \qquad \alpha_0 = -0.2026424;$$

$$n = 2 \qquad \left.\begin{array}{l} \alpha_0 = 10^{-3} \cdot 9.2419, \\ \alpha_1 = -0.280922; \end{array}\right\}$$

$$n = 3 \qquad \left.\begin{array}{l} \alpha_0 = -10^{-4} \cdot 1.249, \\ \alpha_1 = 10^{-2} \cdot 1.35979, \\ \alpha_2 = -0.296814. \end{array}\right\}$$

The characteristic equation (14) (Chapter I, §3) for determining the eigenvalues of A_n in each case becomes

$n = 1$ $\quad P_1(\lambda) = \lambda + \alpha_0 = \lambda - 0.2026424 = 0;$

$n = 2$ $\quad P_2(\lambda) = \lambda^2 + \alpha_1 \lambda + \alpha_0 = \lambda^2 - 0.280922\lambda + 10^{-3} \cdot 9.2419 = 0;$

$n = 3$ $\quad P_3(\lambda) = \lambda^3 + \alpha_2 \lambda^2 + \alpha_1 \lambda + \alpha_0$

$\qquad\qquad = \lambda^3 - 0.296814\lambda^2 + 10^{-2} \cdot 1.35979\lambda - 10^{-4} \cdot 1.249 = 0.$

The roots of these equations provide the following approximations to the eigenvalues of A:

$$n = 1 \qquad \lambda_1 = 0.2026424;$$

$$n = 2 \qquad \lambda_1 = 0.242871,$$
$$\lambda_2 = 10^{-2} \cdot 3.8053;$$

$$n = 3 \qquad \lambda_1 = 0.242963,$$
$$\lambda_2 + 10^{-2} \cdot 4.145,$$
$$\lambda_3 = 10^{-2} \cdot 1.2.$$

On setting $\mu = 1/\lambda$, we arrive at the reciprocal eigenvalues of the original problem. For comparison sake, the accompanying table gives the values of the first one computed by the Rayleigh-Ritz method (S. Mikhlin [1], Scarborough [1]) and the "exact" values of the first three found by Newton's method using

$$\sqrt{\mu} + \tan \sqrt{\mu} = 0.$$

	Method of Moments	Rayleigh-Ritz Method	"Exact" Values
$n = 1$	$\mu_1 = 4.93$	$\mu_1 = 4.93$	
$n = 2$	$\mu_1 = 4.1174$ $\mu_2 = 26.27$	$\mu_1 = 4.59$	
$n = 3$	$\mu_1 = 4.11585$ $\mu_2 = 24.20$ $\mu_3 = 80$	$\mu_1 = 4.40$	$\mu_1 = 4.11585$ $\mu_2 = 24.14$ $\mu_3 = 63.61$

CHAPTER III

The Method of Moments for Self-Adjoint Operators

I. Self-Adjoint Operators

A bounded operator is self-adjoint if it coincides with its adjoint, that is, $A = A^*$ and

$$(Ax, y) = (x, Ay)$$

for any x and y in H. The *bounds of a self-adjoint operator* are respectively the smallest number m and largest number M for which

$$m(x, x) \leqq (Ax, x) \leqq M(x, x) \tag{1}$$

for every x in H.

If $m > 0$, the operator A is called *positive definite*.

We first consider a self-adjoint operator A in some finite dimensional space. In n-dimensional space, we may introduce an orthogonal coordinate system whose basis vectors are elements $y_1, y_2, \ldots, y_n$ having the usual properties

$$(y_i, y_k) = \begin{cases} 1 & i = k, \\ 0 & i \neq k. \end{cases}$$

Let us examine the eigenvalue question. Consider the equation

$$Au = \lambda u. \tag{2}$$

The eigenvalues λ are all real for

$$\lambda = \frac{(Au, u)}{(u, u)}$$

and the scalar product $(Au, u) = (u, Au) = \overline{(Au, u)}$ is real.

Now representing the eigenelement u as a sum of components along the coordinate axes,

$$u = a_1 y_1 + a_2 y_2 + \ldots + a_n y_n, \tag{3}$$

and taking the scalar product of (2) with the respective basis vectors, we arrive at the following system of linear homogeneous equations:

$$\left.\begin{aligned}
a_1(Ay_1, y_1) + a_2(Ay_2, y_1) + \ldots + a_n(Ay_n, y_1) &= \lambda a_1, \\
a_1(Ay_1, y_2) + a_2(Ay_2, y_2) + \ldots + a_n(Ay_n, y_2) &= \lambda a_2, \\
\cdot \quad \cdot \quad \cdot \quad \cdot \quad \cdot \quad \cdot \quad \cdot \quad \cdot \quad \cdot \quad \cdot \quad \cdot \quad \cdot \quad \cdot \quad \cdot \\
a_1(Ay_1, y_n) + a_2(Ay_2, y_n) + \ldots + a_n(Ay_n, y_n) &= \lambda a_n.
\end{aligned}\right\} \tag{4}$$

Equating to zero the determinant of the system, we obtain the characteristic equation for the eigenvalues, namely,

$$\begin{vmatrix}
(Ay_1, y_1) - \lambda & (Ay_2, y_1) \ldots (Ay_n, y_1) \\
(Ay_1, y_2) & (Ay_2, y_2) - \lambda \ldots (Ay_n, y_2) \\
\cdot \quad \cdot \quad \cdot \quad \cdot \quad \cdot \quad \cdot \quad \cdot \quad \cdot \quad \cdot \quad \cdot \quad \cdot \\
(Ay_1, y_n) & (Ay_2, y_n) \ldots (Ay_n, y_n) - \lambda
\end{vmatrix} = 0. \tag{5}$$

For simplicity, suppose that equation (5) has n distinct (real) roots $\lambda_1, \lambda_2, \ldots, \lambda_n$. To each λ_k, there corresponds one eigenelement u_k, defined to within an arbitrary factor, which may be found by solving the system (4) and then making use of (3). The arbitrary factor may always be chosen so that u_k is normalized with $\|u_k\| = 1$.

The eigenelements u_k corresponding to the distinct eigenvalues λ_k are mutually orthogonal. For, let

$$Au_k = \lambda_k u_k,$$

$$Au_i = \lambda_i u_i.$$

The scalar product of the first equation with u_i and the second with u_k and subtraction of the results yields

$$(Au_k, u_i) - (u_k, Au_i) = (\lambda_k - \lambda_i)(u_k, u_i).$$

Hence, when $\lambda_k \neq \lambda_i$, it follows that

$$(u_k, u_i) = 0.$$

Thus, the set of eigenelements may be taken as the basis vectors of a new coordinate system in the space, and hence each element x of H can be represented as

$$x = (x, u_1)u_1 + (x, u_2)u_2 + \ldots + (x, u_n)u_n.$$

We now introduce the notion of spectral function of an operator. Let us arrange the eigenvalues of A in increasing order of magnitude:

$$\lambda_1 < \lambda_2 < \ldots < \lambda_n.$$

The *spectral function* of A, denoted by $\mathscr{E}_\lambda$, is defined to be the family of projections determined by the set of relations

$$\mathscr{E}_\lambda x = 0 \qquad\qquad\qquad\qquad \lambda < \lambda_1$$

$$\mathscr{E}_\lambda x = (x, u_1)u_1 \qquad\qquad\qquad \lambda_1 \leqq \lambda < \lambda_2$$

$$\mathscr{E}_\lambda x = (x, u_1)u_1 + (x, u_2)u_2 \qquad\quad \lambda_2 \leqq \lambda < \lambda_3$$

$$\cdot \quad \cdot \quad \cdot \quad \cdot \quad \cdot \quad \cdot \quad \cdot \quad \cdot \quad \cdot \quad \cdot \quad \cdot \quad \cdot \quad \cdot \quad \cdot \quad \cdot \quad \cdot$$

$$\mathscr{E}_\lambda x = (x, u_1)u_1 + \ldots + (x, u_{n-1})u_{n-1} \quad \lambda_{n-1} \leqq \lambda < \lambda_n$$

$$\mathscr{E}_\lambda x = (x, u_1)u_1 + \ldots + (x, u_n)u_n = x \qquad \lambda \geqq \lambda_n$$

for any element x in H.

The real function $(\mathscr{E}_\lambda x, x)$ has the form

$$(\mathscr{E}_\lambda x, x) = 0 \qquad\qquad\qquad (\lambda < \lambda_1),$$

$$(\mathscr{E}_\lambda x, x) = |(x, u_1)|^2 \qquad\qquad (\lambda_1 \leqq \lambda < \lambda_2),$$

$$\cdot \quad \cdot \quad \cdot \quad \cdot \quad \cdot \quad \cdot \quad \cdot \quad \cdot \quad \cdot \quad \cdot \quad \cdot \quad \cdot \quad \cdot$$

$$(\mathscr{E}_\lambda x, x) = \sum_{k=1}^{n-1} |(x, u_k)|^2 \qquad (\lambda_{n-1} \leqq \lambda < \lambda_n),$$

$$(\mathscr{E}_\lambda x, x) = \| x \|^2 \qquad\qquad\qquad (\lambda \geqq \lambda_n).$$

Thus, $(\mathscr{E}_\lambda x, x)$ is constant on those ranges of λ where A has no eigenvalues and increases by jumps at each eigenvalue λ_k equal to the amount $|(x, u_k)|^2$.

If we let $\Delta_k \mathscr{E}_\lambda$ denote the value of the jump in the projection, that is,

$$\Delta_k \mathscr{E}_\lambda x = (x, u_k)u_k,$$

the expression

$$Ax = \lambda_1 (x, u_1)u_1 + \lambda_2 (x, u_2)u_2 + \ldots + \lambda_n (x, u_n)u_n \qquad (6)$$

can be written in the form

$$Ax = \sum_{k=1}^{n} \lambda_k \Delta_k \mathscr{E}_\lambda x. \tag{6'}$$

A similar formula holds for any arbitrary bounded self-adjoint operator, namely,

$$Ax = \int_m^M \lambda \, d\mathscr{E}_\lambda x,$$

in which the spectral function $\mathscr{E}_\lambda$ of the operator A is understood to be a family of projections depending on the real parameter λ such that

(1) $\mathscr{E}_\lambda$ is non-decreasing with increasing λ, that is, if $\mu > \lambda$, then the subspace into which $\mathscr{E}_\mu$ projects contains the subspace into which $\mathscr{E}_\lambda$ projects;

(2) $\mathscr{E}_m = 0$, $\mathscr{E}_M = I$;

(3) $\mathscr{E}_\lambda$ is continuous from the right, i.e.,

$$\lim_{\lambda \to \lambda' + 0} \mathscr{E}_\lambda = \mathscr{E}_{\lambda'}.$$

The set of points at which the spectral function $\mathscr{E}_\lambda$ changes, or in other words, the set of points at which the monotonic real function $(\mathscr{E}_\lambda x, x)$ increases for any x in H is called the *spectrum* of the operator. The values of λ where $\mathscr{E}_\lambda$ increases by jumps are the eigenvalues of A. The points at which $\mathscr{E}_\lambda$ increases continuously constitute its *continuous spectrum*. As we saw before, the spectrum of a self-adjoint operator in finite dimensional space consists only of a finite number of eigenvalues.

Now consider (6) and apply A to both sides. This yields

$$A^2 x = \lambda_1^2 (x, u_1) u_1 + \lambda_2^2 (x, u_2) u_2 + \ldots + \lambda_n^2 (x, u_n) u_n.$$

For any power of the operator, we have

$$A^m x = \lambda_1^m (x, u_1) u_1 + \lambda_2^m (x, u_2) u_2 + \ldots + \lambda_n^m (x, u_n) u_n.$$

This formula may be extended to any function of A by letting

$$(A)x = f(\lambda_1)(x, u_1) u_1 + f(\lambda_2)(x, u_2) u_2 + \ldots + f(\lambda_n)(x, u_n) u_n$$

or

$$f(A)x = \sum_{k=1}^{n} f(\lambda_k) \Delta_k \mathscr{E}_\lambda x.$$

The following formula then obviously holds:

$$_1(A) f_2 (A)x = \sum_{k=1}^{n} f_1 (\lambda_k) f_2 (\lambda_k) \Delta_k \mathscr{E}_\lambda x.$$

We point out one important property of a function of an operator. In the definition of $f(A)$, just the values of $f(\lambda)$ at the points λ_k are involved, and so $\phi(A) = f(A)$ whenever $\phi(\lambda_k) = f(\lambda_k)$ $(k = 1, 2, \ldots, n)$.

In a similar way, we may define a continuous function of any bounded self-adjoint operator by

$$f(A) = \int_m^M f(\lambda)\, d\mathscr{E}_\lambda, \tag{7}$$

in which the only values of the function that matter are those at the points of the spectrum of the operator, where $d\mathscr{E}_\lambda \neq 0$. The following formula holds:

$$f_1(A)f_2(A) = \int_m^M f_1(\lambda)f_2(\lambda)\, d\mathscr{E}_\lambda. \tag{8}$$

The norm of $f(A)$ can be estimated as follows. Suppose $\left| f(\lambda) \right| \leq C$. Then

$$\left\| f(A)x \right\| \leq \left\| \int_m^M C\, d\mathscr{E}_\lambda x \right\| = C \left\| x \right\|$$

and

$$\left\| f(A) \right\| \leq C. \tag{9}$$

Let us consider some examples of functions of an operator. The inverse operator A^{-1} is given by the integral

$$A^{-1} = \int_m^M \frac{1}{\lambda}\, d\mathscr{E}_\lambda. \tag{10}$$

According to (8), we have

$$AA^{-1}x = A^{-1}Ax = \int_m^M \frac{\lambda}{\lambda}\, d\mathscr{E}_\lambda x = \mathscr{E}_M x - \mathscr{E}_m x = x.$$

Suppose no part of the spectrum of the operator lies within the interval $[-\sigma, \sigma]$. Since λ^{-1} is bounded outside this interval, namely, $\left| \lambda^{-1} \right| \leq \sigma^{-1}$, it follows that A^{-1} is a bounded operator and (9) shows that

$$\left\| A^{-1} \right\| \leq \frac{1}{\sigma}.$$

The converse statement is also true: if A^{-1} is a bounded operator, then an interval $[-\sigma, \sigma]$ exists containing no part of the spectrum of A.

As a second example, consider the Cauchy problem for the equation

$$\frac{\partial x}{\partial t} = Ax,$$

where $x(t)$ is an element of H, and A is a bounded, self-adjoint operator. Let $x = x_0$ for $t = 0$. Then the solution of the equation is expressible as

$$x(t) = e^{At}x_0 = \int_m^M e^{\lambda t}\, d\mathscr{E}_\lambda x_0.$$

The spectrum of a completely continuous self-adjoint operator consists entirely of eigenvalues, and if they are indexed in decreasing order of magnitude, then $|\lambda_n| \to 0$ as $n \to \infty$. Every element of the form Ax can be expanded in terms of an orthonormalized system of eigenelements u_k:

$$Ax = \sum_{i=1}^{\infty} \lambda_i (x, u_i) u_i.$$

If zero is not an eigenvalue, then a similar expansion holds for any x in H:

$$x = \sum_{i=1}^{\infty} (x, u_i) u_i.$$

The eigenelements u_i extremize the expression $(Ax, x)/\|x\|^2$, and $\lambda_i = (Au_i, u_i)/\|u_i\|^2$.

2. The Problem of Moments in Hilbert Space for Self-Adjoint Operators

The self-adjointness of a given operator A greatly simplifies the solution of the problem of moments and makes possible the development of a number of useful algorithms for solving corresponding linear problems.

The solution of linear problems involving finite symmetric matrices has been investigated by C. Lanczos [1], [2], L. Lyusternik [2], and M. Hestenes and E. Stiefel [1]. It is true their point of departure was the Chebyshev-Markov classical scalar problem of moments for the quadratic functional (Ax, x). However, in the case of a self-adjoint operator, the scalar problem of moments is completely equivalent to the operator problem since assigning the operator A is completely equivalent to assigning its corresponding quadratic functional (Ax, x).

The methods of Lanczos and Lyusternik were subsequently extended to completely continuous self-adjoint operators by W. Karush [1] and I. Stesin [1].

A different approach to the question and the use of different methods of solving the problem of moments have led to the development of formally different but essentially very similar methods of solving linear problems.

The problem of moments in Hilbert space makes possible the treatment of all these methods from a more general standpoint as well as the broadening of their range of applicability to a very wide class of self-adjoint operators.

Let A be a prescribed self-adjoint bounded linear operator in Hilbert space H.

Starting with an arbitrarily chosen element z_0, we form the sequence of iterations

$$z_0, \quad z_1 = A z_0, \ldots, z_n = A z_{n-1} = A^n z_0, \ldots$$

The solution of the problem of moments

$$\left. \begin{array}{l} z_k = A^k z_0 = A_n^k z_0 \quad (k = 0, 1, \ldots, n-1), \\[2mm] E_n z_n = E_n A^n z_0 = A_n^n z_0 \end{array} \right\} \tag{11}$$

yields a sequence of operators A_n, each defined on its own subspace H_n generated by all possible linear combinations of $z_0, z_1, \ldots, z_{n-1}$. As before, E_n denotes the operator projecting onto the subspace H_n. Since $A_n = E_n A E_n$ [Cf. (23), Chapter I], A_n is also self-adjoint. To determine its spectrum, we make use of Lanczos' method of successive orthogonalization [1]. Let

$$p_0 = z_0$$

and then consider the element

$$p_1 = A z_0 - a_0 z_0.$$

The coefficient a_0 can easily be determined so as to make p_1 orthogonal to p_0:

$$(p_1, p_0) = (A p_0, p_0) - a_0 (p_0, p_0) = 0.$$

Hence, $$a_0 = \frac{(A p_0, p_0)}{(p_0, p_0)}.$$

Now, define $$p_2 = A p_1 - a_1 p_1 - b_0 p_0.$$

The requirement that p_2 be orthogonal to p_0 and p_1 results in the conditions

$$(p_2, p_0) = (Ap_1, p_0) - b_0 (p_0, p_0) = 0,$$

$$(p_2, p_1) = (Ap_1, p_1) - a_1 (p_1, p_1) = 0.$$

Thus, $\quad a_1 = \dfrac{(Ap_1, p_1)}{(p_1, p_1)}, \quad b_0 = \dfrac{(Ap_1, p_0)}{(p_0, p_0)} = \dfrac{(p_1, Ap_0)}{(p_0, p_0)} = \dfrac{(p_1, p_1)}{(p_0, p_0)}.$

It is easy to see that in general

$$p_{k+1} = (A - a_k I)p_k - b_{k-1} p_{k-1}, \tag{12}$$

where $\quad a_k = \dfrac{(Ap_k, p_k)}{(p_k, p_k)}, \quad b_{k-1} = \dfrac{(p_k, Ap_{k-1})}{(p_{k-1}, p_{k-1})} = \dfrac{(p_k, p_k)}{(p_{k-1}, p_{k-1})}.$

The elements p_k are mutually orthogonal, i.e. $(p_k, p_i) = 0$ for $i \neq k$, and

$$p_k = P_k(A)z_0, \tag{13}$$

with $P_k(A)$ a k-th degree polynomial in A. The polynomials $P_k(\lambda)$ each have leading coefficients of one and satisfy the following recursion relations analogous to (12):

$$\left. \begin{array}{c} P_{k+1}(\lambda) = (\lambda - a_k)P_k(\lambda) - b_{k-1} P_{k-1}(\lambda), \\ b_{-1} = 0, \quad P_0 \equiv 1. \end{array} \right\} \tag{12'}$$

Consider now the problem of moments. In view of (13) and of the definition of A_n,

$$p_k = P_k(A)z_0 = P_k(A_n)z_0 \in H_n \quad (k = 0, 1, \dots, n-1).$$

Thus, the elements $p_0, p_1, \dots, p_{n-1}$ form an orthogonal set in the subspace H_n. Let us compute $P_n(A_n)z_0$.

By definition, $P_n(\lambda)$ is an n-th degree polynomial with a leading coefficient of one. Therefore, making use of (11), we conclude that

$$P_n(A_n)z_0 = E_n P_n(A)z_0 = E_n p_n.$$

On the other hand, p_n is orthogonal to each of the elements $p_0, \dots, p_{n-1}$ comprising a complete orthogonal set in the subspace H_n. Hence,

$$E_n p_n = (p_n, p_0)\frac{p_0}{\|p_0\|^2} + (p_n, p_1)\frac{p_1}{\|p_1\|^2} + \dots + (p_n, p_{n-1})\frac{p_{n-1}}{\|p_{n-1}\|^2} = 0$$

and

$$P_n(A_n)z_0 = 0. \tag{13'}$$

A comparison of this equation with equation (10) of Chapter I shows that the polynomials $P_n(\lambda)$ introduced above coincide with the polynomials $P_n(\lambda)$ resulting in Chapter I. Thus, the roots of

$$P_n(\lambda) = 0$$

are the eigenvalues of the operator A_n.

The corresponding eigenelements could be obtained from the formulas (13) and (13') of Chapter I. However they may be expressed directly in terms of $p_0, p_1, \ldots, p_{n-1}$. Let

$$A_n u_k = \lambda_k u_k,$$

with λ_k a root of $P_n(\lambda)$. We look for a u_k of the form

$$u_k = \sum_{j=0}^{n-1} \frac{(u_k, p_j)}{\| p_j \|^2} p_j.$$

Since A_n is self-adjoint, its eigenelements form a complete orthonormal set in H_n. Expanding p_j in terms of the eigenelements, we obtain

$$p_j = P_j(A_n)z_0 = \sum_{k=0}^{n-1} P_j(\lambda_k)(z_0, u_k)u_k,$$

and hence $$(u_k, p_j) = P_j(\lambda_k)(z_0, u_k).$$

We can thus express u_k as

$$u_k = C \sum_{j=0}^{n-1} P_j(\lambda_k)p_j.$$

The constant C must be chosen so as to assure normalization. The resulting formula is

$$u_k = \frac{1}{\sqrt{\left(\sum_{j=0}^{n-1} P_j^2(\lambda_k) \| p_j \|^2 \right)}} \sum_{j=0}^{n-1} P_j(\lambda_k)p_j. \tag{14}$$

Therefore, a knowledge of the set of polynomials $P_k(\lambda)$ makes it a simple matter to compute the entire spectrum of A_n.

In view of the importance of the question, we indicate another way of computing $P_k(\lambda)$, which is based on continued fractions. We first expand z_0 in terms of the eigenelements of A_n (this is possible because z_0 belongs to all H_n):

$$z_0 = \sum_{k=0}^{n-1} a_k u_k.$$

Now consider the function

$$\phi(\lambda) = \frac{a_0^2}{\lambda - \lambda_0} + \frac{a_1^2}{\lambda - \lambda_1} + \ldots + \frac{a_{n-1}^2}{\lambda - \lambda_{n-1}}, \quad = z_0^T (\lambda I - A)^{-1} z_0$$

where $\lambda_0, \lambda_1, \ldots, \lambda_{n-1}$ are the eigenvalues of A_n. We look for an expansion of $\phi(\lambda)$ in inverse powers of λ of the form

$$\phi(\lambda) = \frac{c_0}{\lambda} + \frac{c_1}{\lambda^2} + \frac{c_2}{\lambda^3} + \ldots + \frac{c_s}{\lambda^{s+1}} + \ldots = \sum_{s=0}^{\infty} \frac{c_s}{\lambda^{s+1}}. \tag{15}$$

Sidestepping the question of convergence, we formally determine the coefficients in the series. We first write

$$\frac{a_k^2}{\lambda - \lambda_k} = \frac{a_k^2}{\lambda} \cdot \sum_{s=0}^{\infty} \left(\frac{\lambda_k}{\lambda}\right)^s$$

and hence
$$\phi(\lambda) = \sum_{k=0}^{n-1} \frac{a_k^2}{\lambda - \lambda_k} = \sum_{s=0}^{\infty} \left[\sum_{k=0}^{n-1} a_k^2 \lambda_k^s\right] \frac{1}{\lambda^{s+1}}.$$

Therefore,
$$c_s = \sum_{k=0}^{n-1} a_k^2 \lambda_k^s.$$

On the other hand,
$$z_s = A_n^s z_0 = \sum_{k=0}^{n-1} a_k \lambda_k^s u_k,$$

and so
$$(z_s, z_0) = \sum_{k=0}^{n-1} a_k^2 \lambda_k^s = c_s \quad (s = 0, 1, \ldots, n-1).$$

In general, for any i and k, it can be easily shown that

$$c_{i+k} = (A_n^i z_0, A_n^k z_0)$$

on account of the self-adjointness of A_n.

The problem of moments also provides a way of computing the coefficients c_0 up to c_{2n-2} inclusive, namely,

$$c_{i+k} = (z_i, z_k) \quad (i + k < 2n - 1).$$

This is a consequence of the definition of A_n [Cf. (11)].

We now proceed to find the polynomial $P_n(\lambda)$. Since the λ_k are its roots, and since its leading coefficient is one, we can write

$$\phi(\lambda) = \sum_{k=0}^{n-1} \frac{a_k^2}{\lambda - \lambda_k} = \frac{Q_{n-1}(\lambda)}{P_n(\lambda)} = \frac{c_0}{\lambda} + \frac{c_1}{\lambda^2} + \ldots,$$

in which $Q_{n-1}(\lambda)$ is some $(n-1)$st degree polynomial. The multiplication of both sides of this equation by $P_n(\lambda)$ leads to

$$Q_{n-1}(\lambda) = P_n(\lambda)\left(\frac{c_0}{\lambda} + \frac{c_1}{\lambda^2} + \dots\right).$$

Let
$$P_n(\lambda) = \sum_{s=0}^{n} \alpha_s^{(n)}\lambda^s,$$

with $\alpha_s^{(n)} = 1$. Then

$$\sum_{s=0}^{n} \alpha_s^{(n)}\lambda^s \cdot \sum_{j=0}^{\infty} \frac{c_j}{\lambda^{j+1}}$$

$$= \sum_{j=-n}^{\infty} \frac{1}{\lambda^{j+1}} \ (c_j\alpha_0^{(n)} + \dots + c_{j+n-1}\alpha_{n-1}^{(n)} + c_{j+n}) = Q_{n-1}(\lambda).$$

Upon equating to zero the coefficients of negative powers of λ, we obtain

$$c_j\alpha_0^{(n)} + c_{j+1}\alpha_1^{(n)} + \dots + c_{j+n-1}\alpha_{n-1}^{(n)} + c_{j+n} = 0, \quad j \geq 0. \quad (16)$$

Only n of these relations corresponding to $j = 0, 1, \dots, n-1$ are linearly independent, the others being linear combinations of them. The system (16) corresponds exactly to the previously obtained system (11) of Chapter I.

Let us now derive recursion formulas for the coefficients of $P_n(\lambda)$. In the equality

$$Q_k(\lambda) = P_{k+1}(\lambda)\left(\frac{c_0}{\lambda} + \frac{c_1}{\lambda^2} + \dots + \frac{c_j}{\lambda^{j+1}} + \dots\right)$$

we replace $P_{k+1}(\lambda)$ by the recurrence relation (12'). This yields

$$Q_k(\lambda) = (\lambda - a_k)P_k(\lambda)\left(\frac{c_0}{\lambda} + \frac{c_1}{\lambda^2} + \dots + \frac{c_{k-1}}{\lambda^k} + \frac{c_k}{\lambda^{k+1}} + \dots\right)$$

$$- b_{k-1}P_{k-1}(\lambda)\left(\frac{c_0}{\lambda} + \frac{c_1}{\lambda^2} + \dots + \frac{c_{k-1}}{\lambda^k} + \frac{c_k}{\lambda^{k+1}} + \dots\right).$$

Inserting
$$P_k(\lambda) = \sum_{j=0}^{k} \alpha_j^{(k)}\lambda^j$$

and then equating the coefficient of λ^{-k} to zero, we obtain by means of (16)

$$c_k\alpha_0^{(k)} + c_{k+1}\alpha_1^{(k)} + \dots + c_{2k-1}\alpha_{k-1}^{(k)} + c_{2k}$$

$$- b_{k-1}(c_{k-1}\alpha_0^{(k-1)} + c_k\alpha_1^{(k-1)} + \dots + c_{2k-3}\alpha_{k-2}^{(k-1)} + c_{2k-2}) = 0.$$

A similar operation on the coefficient of λ^{-k-1} yields

$$c_{k+1}\alpha_0^{(k)} + c_{k+2}\alpha_1^{(k)} + \ldots + c_{2k}\alpha_{k-1}^{(k)} + c_{2k+1}$$
$$- a_k(c_k\alpha_0^{(k)} + c_{k+1}\alpha_1^{(k)} + \ldots + c_{2k-1}\alpha_{k-1}^{(k)} + c_{2k})$$
$$- b_{k-1}(c_k\alpha_0^{(k-1)} + c_{k+1}\alpha_1^{(k-1)} + \ldots + c_{2k-2}\alpha_{k-2}^{(k-1)} + c_{2k-1}) = 0.$$

Introducing the notation

$$h_k = c_k\alpha_0^{(k)} + c_{k+1}\alpha_1^{(k)} + \ldots + c_{2k-1}\alpha_{k-1}^{(k)} + c_{2k},$$

$$h_{k+\frac{1}{2}} = c_{k+1}\alpha_0^{(k)} + c_{k+2}\alpha_1^{(k)} + \ldots + c_{2k}\alpha_{k-1}^{(k)} + c_{2k+1},$$

we have

$$\left. \begin{array}{c} b_{k-1} = \dfrac{h_k}{h_{k-1}}, \\[3mm] a_k = \dfrac{h_{k+\frac{1}{2}}}{h_k} - b_{k-1}\dfrac{h_{k-\frac{1}{2}}}{h_k} = \dfrac{h_{k+\frac{1}{2}}}{h_k} - \dfrac{h_{k-\frac{1}{2}}}{h_{k-1}}. \end{array} \right\} \tag{17}$$

The recurrence relation (12′) implies that

$$\sum_{s=0}^{k+1}\alpha_s^{(k+1)}\lambda^s = \sum_{s=0}^{k}\alpha_s^{(k)}\lambda^{s+1} - a_k\sum_{s=0}^{k}\alpha_s^{(k)}\lambda^s - b_{k-1}\sum_{s=0}^{k-1}\alpha_s^{(k-1)}\lambda^s.$$

Hence, upon equating coefficients of like powers of λ, we arrive at recurrence relations for the coefficients, namely,

$$\left. \begin{array}{c} \alpha_{k+1}^{(k+1)} = \alpha_k^{(k)} = 1, \quad \alpha_k^{(k-1)} = 0, \\[2mm] \alpha_s^{(k+1)} = \alpha_{s-1}^{(k)} - a_k\alpha_s^{(k)} - b_{k-1}\alpha_s^{(k-1)} \quad (s = 0, 1, \ldots, k). \end{array} \right\} \tag{18}$$

These formulas express the coefficients of $P_k(\lambda)$ in terms of the scalar products $c_i = (z_{i-k}, z_k)$.

The above method of determining the coefficients of $P_k(\lambda)$ is in reality equivalent to converting the series (15) into a continued fraction. Such a conversion is not unique; the series (15) may be represented as a continued fraction in various ways. As a result, different algorithms may be developed for computing the polynomials $P_k(\lambda)$. However, they all lead to the same recurrence relations (12′) and are therefore merely modifications of the above algorithm.

The equivalence of the operator and scalar problems of moments in the case of a self-adjoint operator enables one to solve the problem by the classical methods of Chebyshev [1], Markov [1], and Stieltjes [1]. It also makes possible the use of continued fractions to investigate the convergence of the processes that the method of moments provides for the solution of linear problems. Just such an approach was suggested by Lyusternik [2] and was later employed by Stesin [1] in problems involving completely continuous self-adjoint operators.

The set of polynomials $P_n(\lambda)$ possesses the very important property of orthogonality from which a number of inferences may be made concerning the distribution of their roots, the eigenvalues of the operators A_n.

Let $\mathscr{E}_\lambda$ be the spectral function of the operator A, so that

$$A = \int_m^M \lambda\, d\mathscr{E}_\lambda,$$

with m the greatest lower bound and M the least upper bound of the spectrum of the operator. Then

$$p_k = P_k(A)z_0 = \int_m^M P_k(\lambda)\, d\mathscr{E}_\lambda z_0,$$

and in view of the orthogonality of the elements p_k,

$$(p_i, p_k) = \int_m^M P_i(\lambda)P_k(\lambda)\, d(\mathscr{E}_\lambda z_0, z_0) = 0 \quad (i \neq k). \tag{19}$$

Thus the polynomials $P_n(\lambda)$ are orthogonal over the interval $[m, M]$ with respect to the non-decreasing function $(\mathscr{E}_\lambda z_0, z_0)$ in the sense of (19). Hence, it can be shown that

(1) the polynomials $P_n(\lambda)$ form a Sturm series, that is, all their roots, which are the eigenvalues of the operators A_n, are real, distinct, and separate one another;

(2) the roots all lie in the interval $[m, M]$, where m and M are the bounds of the spectrum of A;

(3) on any portion of the range of λ where $(\mathscr{E}_\lambda z_0, z_0)$ is a constant, $P_n(\lambda)$ can have no more than one root for each value of n.

[See for example, M. Shohat [1] and Ya. Geronimus [1]].

3. Determination of the Spectrum of a Self-Adjoint Operator

In the preceding section, we gave some methods for computing the eigenvalues and corresponding eigenelements of the operator A_n. Earlier it was shown that if A_n is completely continuous, then the eigenvalues and eigenelements of A_n tend to the eigenvalues and eigen-elements of the given operator when n increases indefinitely. For a bounded self-adjoint operator, the following general theorem holds.

Theorem IX: *If A is a bounded self-adjoint operator and A_n a sequence of solutions of the moment problem* (11), *then the sequence of spectral functions $\mathscr{E}_\lambda^{(n)}$ of the operators A_n converges strongly to the spectral function of A:*

$$\mathscr{E}_\lambda^{(n)} \to \mathscr{E}_\lambda, \quad n \to \infty,$$

in the subspace H_z for all λ not belonging to the discrete spectrum of A.

The proof of the theorem is based on the fact that the sequence A_n converges strongly. A first immediate consequence of the strong convergence of these operators is the strong convergence of polynomials of A_n. To wit, if $P(\mu)$ is any polynomial, then

$$P(A_n) \to P(A).$$

By means of Weierstrass's Theorem on the approximation of continuous functions by polynomials, this result may be extended to any function $u(\mu)$ continuous on the interval $|\mu| \leq \|A\|$.

In particular, let us take $u(\mu)$ to be the function $e_\lambda(\mu)(\mu - \lambda)$, where $e_\lambda(\mu)$ is equal to 1 for $\mu \leq \lambda$ and 0 for $\mu > \lambda$. Then $u(A_n) = \mathscr{E}_\lambda^{(n)}A_n$, $u(A) = \mathscr{E}_\lambda A$, and by virtue of the continuity of $u(\mu)$,

$$\mathscr{E}_\lambda^{(n)}A_n \to \mathscr{E}_\lambda A.$$

Now

$$\left\| \mathscr{E}_\lambda^{(n)}Ax - \mathscr{E}_\lambda Ax \right\| \leq \left\| \mathscr{E}_\lambda^{(n)}(A - A_n)x \right\| + \left\| \mathscr{E}_\lambda^{(n)}A_n x - \mathscr{E}_\lambda Ax \right\|$$

$$\leq \left\| (A - A_n)x \right\| + \left\| \mathscr{E}_\lambda^{(n)}A_n x - \mathscr{E}_\lambda Ax \right\| \to 0$$

and this implies that

$$\mathscr{E}_\lambda^{(n)}A \to \mathscr{E}_\lambda A \quad \text{in} \quad H_z.$$

If λ is not an eigenvalue of A, then A^{-1} exists, is also self-adjoint and

$$\mathscr{E}_\lambda^{(n)}x = \mathscr{E}_\lambda^{(n)}AA^{-1}x \to \mathscr{E}_\lambda AA^{-1}x = \mathscr{E}_\lambda x$$

for each x in the domain of definition of A^{-1}. Since the latter is dense in H_z and since the projections $\mathscr{E}_\lambda^{(n)}$ are uniformly bounded, it follows that

$$\mathscr{E}_\lambda^{(n)} \to \mathscr{E}_\lambda.$$

Obtaining an approximation to the spectral function of a self-adjoint operator by solving the moment problem is closely connected with a variational problem. Suppose A has a discrete spectrum. We shall look for approximations to the eigenelements of the form

$$u^{(n)} = Q_{n-1}(A)z_0 \in H_n,$$

where $Q_{n-1}(\lambda)$ is a polynomial of $(n-1)$st degree. The coefficients of $Q_{n-1}(\lambda)$ and the corresponding eigenvalues will be determined by the variational problem

$$\lambda^{(n)} = \operatorname{extr} \frac{(Au^{(n)}, u^{(n)})}{\| u^{(n)} \|^2}.$$

We first show that the solutions to the variational problem are the eigenvalues and eigenelements of the operator A_n solving the problem of moments.

Since $u^{(n)} \in H_n$ and $E_n u^{(n)} = u^{(n)}$, it follows that

$$(Au^{(n)}, u^{(n)}) = (Au^{(n)}, E_n u^{(n)}) = (E_n A E_n u^{(n)}, u^{(n)}) = (A_n u^{(n)}, u^{(n)}).$$

Thus, in H_n

$$\lambda^{(n)} = \operatorname{extr} \frac{(Au^{(n)}, u^{(n)})}{\| u^{(n)} \|^2} = \operatorname{extr} \frac{(A_n u^{(n)}, u^{(n)})}{\| u^{(n)} \|^2},$$

and hence any $\lambda^{(n)}$ and $u^{(n)}$ furnishing an extremum are an eigenvalue and eigenelement of A_n.

The extremal properties of the solution of the problem of moments make it possible to investigate also the speed of convergence of the process. Let A be completely continuous with $\lambda_0, \lambda_1, \ldots, \lambda_n, \ldots$ its eigenvalues arranged in numerically decreasing order, i.e.,

$$|\lambda_0| > |\lambda_1| > \ldots > |\lambda_n| > \ldots \to 0.$$

Consider the subspace R_m consisting of the elements of H_z orthogonal to the first m eigenelements $u_0, u_1, \ldots, u_{m-1}$. Then if $\lambda_m > 0$,

$$\max \frac{(Ax, x)}{\| x \|^2} = \lambda_m, \quad x \in R_m,$$

or if $\lambda_m < 0$,

$$\min \frac{(Ax, x)}{\| x \|^2} = \lambda_m, \quad x \in R_m.$$

For definiteness, consider the case $\lambda_m > 0$.

We expand the basic element z_0 in terms of the eigenelements of A:

$$z_0 = \sum_{k=0}^{\infty} a_k u_k, \quad a_k = (z_0, u_k).$$

Let
$$x_n = Q_{n-1}(A)z_0 = \sum_{k=0}^{\infty} Q_{n-1}(\lambda_k)a_k u_k,$$

where $Q_{n-1}(\lambda)$ is a polynomial of $(n-1)$st degree, so that $x_n \in H_n$. Moreover, suppose $Q_{n-1}(\lambda_0) = Q_{n-1}(\lambda_1) = \ldots = Q_{n-1}(\lambda_{m-1}) = 0$, then x_n also belongs to R_m. Let $\lambda_{n,m}$ denote a corresponding eigenvalue of the operator A_n [and thus a root of the polynomial $P_n(\lambda)$]. The extremal property of the solution of the moment problem and the fact that $\lambda_m > 0$ then imply

$$\lambda_{n,m} \geqq \frac{(Ax_n, x_n)}{\|x_n\|^2}.$$

Suppose further that

$$Q_{n-1}(\lambda) = (\lambda - \lambda_0)(\lambda - \lambda_1)\ldots(\lambda - \lambda_{m-1})(\lambda - \lambda_{m+1})\ldots(\lambda - \lambda_{n-1}),$$

then

$$x_n = a_m Q_{n-1}(\lambda_m)u_m + \sum_{k=n}^{\infty} a_k Q_{n-1}(\lambda_k)u_k,$$

$$\|x_n\|^2 = a_m^2 Q_{n-1}^2(\lambda_m) + \sum_{k=n}^{\infty} a_k^2 Q_{n-1}^2(\lambda_k),$$

$$(Ax_n, x_n) = \lambda_m a_m^2 Q_{n-1}^2(\lambda_m) + \sum_{k=n}^{\infty} \lambda_k a_k^2 Q_{n-1}^2(\lambda_k),$$

and the inequality becomes

$$\lambda_{n,m} \geqq \frac{\lambda_m + \dfrac{1}{a_m^2}\sum_{k=n}^{\infty}\lambda_k a_k^2 \dfrac{Q_{n-1}^2(\lambda_k)}{Q_{n-1}^2(\lambda_m)}}{1 + \dfrac{1}{a_m^2}\sum_{k=n}^{\infty} a_k^2 \dfrac{Q_{n-1}^2(\lambda_k)}{Q_{n-1}^2(\lambda_m)}}. \tag{20}$$

Let us show that $|Q_{n-1}(\lambda_k)/Q_{n-1}(\lambda_m)| \to 0$ as n tends to infinity. In fact, since $k \geqq n$ and hence $|\lambda_k| < |\lambda_n|$, it follows that

$$|Q_{n-1}(\lambda_k)| \leqq (|\lambda_0| + |\lambda_n|)(|\lambda_1| + |\lambda_n|)\ldots$$
$$\ldots(|\lambda_{m-1}| + |\lambda_n|)(|\lambda_{m+1}| + |\lambda_n|)\ldots(|\lambda_{n-1}| + |\lambda_n|),$$

$$|Q_{n-1}(\lambda_m)| \geqq (|\lambda_0| - |\lambda_m|)(|\lambda_1| - |\lambda_m|)\ldots$$
$$\ldots(|\lambda_{m-1}| - |\lambda_m|)(|\lambda_m| - |\lambda_{m+1}|)\ldots(|\lambda_m| - |\lambda_{n-1}|)$$

and

$$\frac{|Q_{n-1}(\lambda_k)|}{|Q_{n-1}(\lambda_m)|} \leqq \frac{|\lambda_0| + |\lambda_n|}{|\lambda_0| - |\lambda_m|}\ldots\frac{|\lambda_{m-1}| + |\lambda_n|}{|\lambda_{m-1}| - |\lambda_m|}$$
$$\times \frac{|\lambda_{m+1}| + |\lambda_n|}{|\lambda_m| - |\lambda_{m+1}|}\ldots\frac{|\lambda_{n-1}| + |\lambda_n|}{|\lambda_m| - |\lambda_{n-1}|}.$$

But $\{|\lambda_{n-1}|+|\lambda_n|\}/\{|\lambda_m|-|\lambda_{n-1}|\}$ approaches zero for fixed m when $n \to \infty$, and so $|Q_{n-1}(\lambda_k)/Q_{n-1}(\lambda_m)|$ approaches zero when $n \to \infty$.

Discarding small terms of the second order in (20), we have approximately

$$\lambda_{n,m} \geqq \lambda_m - \frac{1}{a_m^2} \sum_{k=n}^{\infty} (\lambda_m - \lambda_k) \frac{Q_{n-1}^2(\lambda_k)}{Q_{n-1}^2(\lambda_m)} a_k^2 \quad (\lambda_m > 0). \tag{21}$$

In the event that $\lambda_m < 0$, the variational problem implies the inequality

$$\lambda_{n,m} \leqq \frac{(Ax_n, x_n)}{\|x_n\|^2}.$$

By repeating the above reasoning, we obtain

$$\lambda_{n,m} \leqq \lambda_m - \frac{1}{a_m^2} \sum_{k=n}^{\infty} (\lambda_m - \lambda_k) \frac{Q_{n-1}^2(\lambda_k)}{Q_{n-1}^2(\lambda_m)} a_k^2 \quad (\lambda_m < 0). \tag{22}$$

An examination of (21) and (22) then yields the following estimate for the general case where λ_m has any sign:

$$|\lambda_m - \lambda_{n,m}| \leqq \frac{1}{a_m^2} \sum_{k=n}^{\infty} |\lambda_m - \lambda_k| \frac{Q_{n-1}^2(\lambda_k)}{Q_{n-1}^2(\lambda_m)} a_k^2$$

$$\leqq \frac{|\lambda_m| + |\lambda_n|}{a_m^2} \left[\frac{|\lambda_0| + |\lambda_n|}{|\lambda_0| - |\lambda_m|} \right]^2 \cdots$$

$$\cdots \left[\frac{|\lambda_{m-1}| + |\lambda_n|}{|\lambda_{m-1}| - |\lambda_m|} \right]^2 \cdots \left[\frac{|\lambda_{n-1}| + |\lambda_n|}{|\lambda_m| - |\lambda_{n-1}|} \right]^2 \sum_{k=n}^{\infty} a_k^2. \tag{23}$$

If the operator A is positive definite and so all $\lambda_k > 0$, the estimate (23) can be replaced by the following:

$$|\lambda_m - \lambda_{n,m}| \leqq \frac{\lambda_m}{a_m^2} \frac{\lambda_0^2}{(\lambda_0 - \lambda_m)^2} \cdots \frac{\lambda_{m-1}^2}{(\lambda_{m-1} - \lambda_m)^2}$$

$$\times \frac{\lambda_{m+1}^2}{(\lambda_m - \lambda_{m+1})^2} \cdots \frac{\lambda_{n-1}^2}{(\lambda_m - \lambda_{n-1})^2} \sum_{k=n}^{\infty} a_k^2. \tag{23'}$$

The above estimates show that the eigenvalues of A_n [the roots of the polynomials $P_n(\lambda)$] tend to those of the given operator A faster than any geometric progression. A similar inference can be made concerning the eigenelements. The inequalities (23) and (23') further imply that the numerically largest eigenvalues are determined most accurately.

In certain problems, it is of importance to compute the eigenvalues lying in some given interval of the spectrum of A.

Suppose the whole spectrum falls in the interval $[m, M]$ and suppose we wish to determine the eigenvalues and corresponding eigenelements lying in $[a, b]$ contained within $[m, M]$. A direct application of the moments method may prove to be inadequate since, first of all, the numerically largest and hence perhaps non-pertinent eigenvalues would be determined, and so to compute the eigenvalues lying in $[a, b]$, it would be necessary to make n large. However, the operator A may be so transformed that one is able to determine most accurately exactly those eigenvalues lying in $[a, b]$.

Let $S(\lambda)$ be a polynomial assuming its maximum value in $[a, b]$ and deviating from zero by as little as possible in $[b, M]$ and $[a, m]$. As [m, a] such an $S(\lambda)$, we may take a polynomial normalized so that $S[(a+b)/2] = 1$. Introduce the operator $B = S(A)$. Then B and A have the same eigenelements:

$$Au_k = \lambda_k u_k, \quad Bu_k = \mu_k u_k,$$

while their eigenvalues are related by

$$\mu_k = S(\lambda_k).$$

Hence, the numerically largest eigenvalues of B correspond exactly to the λ_k lying in the interval $[a, b]$. After first obtaining the μ_k by the method of moments, we can compute the eigenvalues of A in $[a, b]$ by solving the equation

$$S(\lambda) = \mu_k \quad (a \leq \lambda \leq b).$$

4. Solution of Non-Homogeneous Linear Equations with Bounded Self-Adjoint Operators

In this section, we use the solution to the problem of moments to construct a sequence of operators converging to an inverse operator A^{-1}. In so doing, we confine our considerations to the most important case arising in applications where the inverse operator is bounded, or more precisely, where there exists an interval $[-\sigma, \sigma]$ containing no part of the spectrum of A.

Consider a non-homogeneous linear equation of the first kind,

$$Ax = f, \tag{24}$$

with A a bounded, self-adjoint operator and f an element of H_z. Now choose a continuous function $\phi(\lambda)$ on the interval $|\lambda| \leq \|A\|$ equal to λ^{-1} outside $[-\sigma, \sigma]$. Since the spectrum of the operator falls outside $[-\sigma, \sigma]$, it follows that $\phi(A) = A^{-1}$. As mentioned before, the convergence of operators can be extended immediately to that of functions of operators. Therefore, by Theorem II, $\phi(A_n) \to A^{-1}$ in the subspace H_z and so the sequence $x_n = \phi(A_n)f$, or

$$x_n = \int_m^M \phi(\lambda) \, d\mathscr{E}_\lambda^{(n)} f \tag{25}$$

converges strongly to the solution of (24).

The element x_n approximating the solution of (24) may be found directly from (25) since the spectral functions are easy to determine. Let $\lambda_k^{(n)}$ and $u_k^{(n)}$ denote the eigenvalues and eigenelements of A_n. Then

$$\mathscr{E}_\lambda^{(n)} = \sum_k (\, , u_k^{(n)}) u_k^{(n)},$$

where the summation extends over all values of k for which $\lambda_k < \lambda$. The formula (25) thus yields

$$x_n = \sum_{k=0}^{n-1} \phi(\lambda_k^{(n)})(f, u_k^{(n)}) u_k^{(n)}.$$

However, x_n may be determined as a rule without any recourse to the spectrum of A_n.

Consider first the case where A is positive definite, and let its entire spectrum lie in the interval $[m, M]$, with $m > 0$. According to the properties of the orthogonal polynomials mentioned at the end of §2, the eigenvalues of A_n are all positive and lie in the interval $[m, M]$ in which $\phi(\lambda) = \lambda^{-1}$. Therefore,

$$x_n = \int_m^M \phi(\lambda) \, d\mathscr{E}_\lambda^{(n)} f = \int_m^M \frac{1}{\lambda} \, d\mathscr{E}_\lambda^{(n)} f.$$

Now A_n is an operator on the subspace H_n whose elements are linear combinations of $z_0, z_1, \ldots, z_{n-1}$, and $\mathscr{E}_\lambda^{(n)}$ projects each element of H_z onto some part of H_n. Thus, if f_n denotes the projection of f on H_n, i.e., $f_n = E_n f$, then $\mathscr{E}_\lambda^{(n)} f = \mathscr{E}_\lambda^{(n)} f_n$ and

$$x_n = \int_m^M \frac{1}{\lambda} \, d\mathscr{E}_\lambda^{(n)} f_n = A_n^{-1} f_n.$$

Thus, x_n satisfies the equation

$$A_n x_n = f_n, \tag{26}$$

whose solution according to (17) of Chapter I is given by

$$x_n = A_n^{-1}\left[F_{n-1}(A_n) - \frac{F_{n-1}(0)}{P_n(0)}P_n(A_n)\right]z_0,$$

with $F_{n-1}(A_n)z_0 = f_n$. But x_n is an $(n-1)$st degree polynomial in A_n:

$$x_n = Q_{n-1}(A_n)z_0,$$

where

$$Q_{n-1}(\lambda) = \frac{1}{\lambda}\left[F_{n-1}(\lambda) - \frac{F_{n-1}(0)}{P_n(0)}P_n(\lambda)\right].$$

Thus, from the way in which A_n is constructed [Cf. (11)], we have that

$$Q_{n-1}(A_n)z_0 = Q_{n-1}(A)z_0$$

and

$$x_n = A^{-1}\left[F_{n-1}(A) - \frac{F_{n-1}(0)}{P_n(0)}P_n(A)\right]z_0. \tag{27}$$

The successive approximations x_n may be determined for the present case of a positive definite operator by means of the following useful algorithm. Since the eigenvalues of A_n, the roots of $P_n(\lambda)$, are now all positive, $P_n(0)$ vanishes for no value of n and the solution (27) always exists. Let

$$R_n(\lambda) = \frac{P_n(\lambda)}{P_n(0)}.$$

Then the recursion relations (12') become

$$R_{n+1}(\lambda) = \frac{P_n(0)}{P_{n+1}(0)}(\lambda - a_n)R_n(\lambda) - b_{n-1}\frac{P_{n-1}(0)}{P_{n+1}(0)}R_{n-1}(\lambda). \tag{12''}$$

For $\lambda = 0$, we have

$$1 = -a_n\frac{P_n(0)}{P_{n+1}(0)} - b_{n-1}\frac{P_{n-1}(0)}{P_{n+1}(0)}.$$

Now letting $h_n = -P_n(0)/P_{n+1}(0)$, we may write the recursion relations (12'') in the form

$$R_{n+1}(\lambda) = \left(1 + b_{n-1}\frac{P_{n-1}(0)}{P_{n+1}(0)} - h_n\lambda\right)R_n(\lambda)$$

$$- b_{n-1}\frac{P_{n-1}(0)}{P_{n+1}(0)}R_{n-1}(\lambda),$$

or $\dfrac{R_{n+1}(\lambda)-R_n(\lambda)}{-h_n\lambda} = R_n(\lambda)+h_{n-1}\dfrac{b_{n-1}P_{n-1}(0)}{h_nP_{n+1}(0)}\left[\dfrac{R_n(\lambda)-R_{n-1}(\lambda)}{-h_{n-1}\lambda}\right].$

Let $\qquad\qquad\dfrac{R_{n+1}(\lambda)-R_n(\lambda)}{-h_n\lambda} = G_n(\lambda),$

$$h_{n-1}\frac{b_{n-1}P_{n-1}(0)}{h_nP_{n+1}(0)} = \frac{b_{n-1}P_{n-1}^2(0)}{P_n^2(0)} = l_{n-1};$$

then $\qquad\qquad \left.\begin{aligned}R_{n+1}(\lambda) &= R_n(\lambda)-h_n\lambda G_n(\lambda),\\ G_n(\lambda) &= R_n(\lambda)+l_{n-1}G_{n-1}(\lambda),\end{aligned}\right\}$ (28)

where $R_0 = G_0 = 1$.

It is easy to see that $G_n(\lambda)$ is an n-th degree polynomial, since the difference $R_{n+1}(\lambda)-R_n(\lambda)$ involves no constant term and so is exactly divisible by λ.

Along with the polynomials $R_n(\lambda)$ and $G_n(\lambda)$, we next introduce corresponding elements of Hilbert space

$$r_n = R_n(A)z_0, \quad g_n = G_n(A)z_0,$$

which are related by

$$\left.\begin{aligned}r_{n+1} &= r_n-h_nAg_n,\\ g_n &= r_n+l_{n-1}g_{n-1},\end{aligned}\right\}$$ (28')

with $r_0 = g_0 = z_0$.

The elements r_n are obviously mutually orthogonal since they differ from the orthogonal elements p_n by scalar factors.

We now take the scalar product of the first equation of (28') with g_k $(k < n)$ obtaining

$$h_n(Ag_n, g_k) = (r_n-r_{n+1}, g_k).$$

But $\qquad\qquad\qquad g_k = r_k+l_{k-1}g_{k-1}$

and so

$$h_n(Ag_n, g_k) = (r_n-r_{n+1}, r_k+l_{k-1}g_{k-1})$$

$$= l_{k-1}(r_n-r_{n+1}, g_{k-1}) = \ldots = l_{k-1}\cdot l_{k-2}\cdots$$

$$\ldots l_0(r_n-r_{n+1}, g_0) = l_{k-1}\cdot l_{k-2}\ldots l_0\cdot(r_n-r_{n+1}, r_0) = 0.$$

Since $h_n \neq 0$, it follows that $(Ag_n, g_k) = 0$ for $k < n$. However, the self-adjointness property, $(Ag_n, g_k) = (g_n, Ag_k)$, shows that

$$(Ag_n, g_k) = 0 \quad (n \neq k).$$

This property of the sequence g_n is referred to as *A-orthogonality*. It in turn implies the orthogonality of the polynomials $G_n(\lambda)$:

$$\int_m^M G_n(\lambda)G_k(\lambda)\lambda\,d(\mathscr{E}_\lambda z_0, z_0) = 0 \quad (n \neq k).$$

We are now immediately able to compute the coefficients h_n and l_{n-1}. Taking the scalar product of the first equation of (28') with r_n, we conclude that

$$0 = (r_n, r_n) - h_n(Ag_n, r_n),$$

or

$$h_n = \frac{\|r_n\|^2}{(Ag_n, r_n)} = \frac{\|r_n\|^2}{(Ag_n, g_n)}.$$

The scalar product of the second equation of (28') with Ag_{n-1} yields

$$0 = (r_n, Ag_{n-1}) + l_{n-1}(Ag_{n-1}, g_{n-1}).$$

But

$$(r_n, Ag_{n-1}) = \frac{1}{h_{n-1}}(r_n, r_{n-1} - r_n) = -\frac{1}{h_{n-1}}(r_n, r_n),$$

and hence

$$l_{n-1} = -\frac{(r_n, Ag_{n-1})}{(g_{n-1}, Ag_{n-1})} = \frac{\|r_n\|^2}{h_{n-1}(g_{n-1}, Ag_{n-1})} = \frac{\|r_n\|^2}{\|r_{n-1}\|^2}.$$

Let us now return to the solution of equation (26). From (27), we have

$$x_n = A^{-1}[F_{n-1}(A) - F_{n-1}(0)R_n(A)]z_0 = A^{-1}[f_n - F_{n-1}(0)r_n],$$

where $F_{n-1}(A)z_0 = E_n f = f_n$.

Since $r_0, r_1, \ldots, r_{n-1}$ form an orthogonal basis in H_n, it follows that

$$f_n = E_n f = \sum_{k=0}^{n-1} (f, r_k)\frac{r_k}{\|r_k\|^2},$$

$$F_{n-1}(0) = \sum_{k=0}^{n-1} \frac{(f, r_k)}{\|r_k\|^2}R_k(0) = \sum_{k=0}^{n-1}\frac{(f, r_k)}{\|r_k\|^2}.$$

Making use of the first equation of (28'), we finally obtain

$$\begin{aligned}
x_{n+1} &= A^{-1}[F_n(A) - F_n(0)R_{n+1}(A)]z_0 \\
&= A^{-1}[f_{n+1} - F_n(0)r_{n+1}] \\
&= A^{-1}\left[f_n + \frac{(f, r_n)r_n}{\|r_n\|^2} - \left(F_{n-1}(0) + \frac{(f, r_n)}{\|r_n\|^2}\right)(r_n - h_n Ag_n)\right] \\
&= A^{-1}\left[f_n - F_{n-1}(0)r_n + h_n\left(F_{n-1}(0) + \frac{(f, r_n)}{\|r_n\|^2}\right)Ag_n\right] \\
&= x_n + h_n F_n(0)g_n.
\end{aligned}$$

Thus, the successive approximations x_n to the solution of the equation $Ax = f$ can be determined by means of the following algorithm:

$$x_{n+1} = x_n + h_n F_n(0) g_n,$$

$$\left.\begin{array}{c} g_n = r_n + l_{n-1} g_{n-1}, \qquad\qquad h_{n-1} = \dfrac{\| r_{n-1} \|^2}{(Ag_{n-1}, g_{n-1})}, \\[4mm] r_n = r_{n-1} - h_{n-1} A g_{n-1}, \qquad l_{n-1} = \dfrac{\| r_n \|^2}{\| r_{n-1} \|^2}, \\[4mm] F_n(0) = F_{n-1}(0) + \dfrac{(f, r_n)}{\| r_n \|^2}, \\[4mm] r_0 = g_0 = z_0, \quad F_0(0) = \dfrac{(f, z_0)}{\| z_0 \|^2}. \end{array}\right\} \tag{29}$$

We summarize the above results in the form of a theorem.

Theorem X: *Let A be a bounded self-adjoint positive (negative) definite operator defined on the Hilbert space H and let z_0 be any element of H. Then a sequence x_n exists, obtainable from* (27) *or, equivalently,* (29) *which converges (strongly) to the solution x of equation* (24), *provided f is in the subspace H_z.*

If in particular z_0 is chosen to be f, then (27) simplifies to

$$x_n = A^{-1} \left[I - \frac{P_n(A)}{P_n(0)} \right] f, \tag{27'}$$

and the algorithm described by (29) assumes the form

$$x_{n+1} = x_n + h_n g_n,$$

$$\left.\begin{array}{c} g_n = r_n + l_{n-1} g_{n-1}, \qquad\qquad h_{n-1} = \dfrac{\| r_{n-1} \|^2}{(Ag_{n-1}, g_{n-1})}, \\[4mm] r_n = r_{n-1} - h_{n-1} A g_{n-1}, \qquad l_{n-1} = \dfrac{\| r_n \|^2}{\| r_{n-1} \|^2}, \\[4mm] r_0 = g_0 = f, \quad f - Ax_n = r_n. \end{array}\right\} \tag{29'}$$

The algorithm (29) is known as the *method of conjugate gradients* and was developed by Hestenes and Stiefel [1] for solving a system of linear algebraic equations with a positive definite coefficient matrix.

The advantage that the more general formulas (27) and (29) have over (27') and (29') is that if an approximate solution has been found for one right-hand side f, then the solution for any other f can be determined directly without having to recompute the polynomials $P_n(A)$, g_n, and r_n.

The resultant approximate solution is closely tied up with a variational problem. It is well-known that the solution of $Ax = f$ minimizes the quadratic functional

$$I(x) = (Ax, x) - 2(f, x).$$ (30)

Let us show that if an approximate solution is sought in H_n, then the x_n given by (27) or (29) minimizes the functional (30) in H_n.

If $x \in H_n$, then $E_n x = x$ and $(f, x) = (f, E_n x) = (f_n, x)$. Furthermore, $(Ax, x) = (AE_n x, E_n x) = (E_n AE_n x, x) = (A_n x, x)$. Thus, in H_n

$$I(x) = (A_n x, x) - 2(f_n, x).$$

Consequently, the solution x_n of $A_n x_n = f_n$ minimizes the functional $I(x)$ in H_n. Hence, among other things, this means the method is very closely related to Kantorovich's "multi-step" method of steepest descent [3].

Having the approximate solution expressed in the form (27) and (29) enables us to derive an error estimate.

Let x_* be the required solution, and suppose η_n is the error in the approximate solution x_n. Then

$$\eta_n = x_* - x_n = A^{-1}f - x_n = A^{-1}(f - f_n)$$

$$+ A^{-1}\frac{F_{n-1}(0)}{P_n(0)} P_n(A)z_0 = A^{-1}(f - f_n) + A^{-1}F_{n-1}(0)r_n.$$

Since the norm of the inverse operator does not exceed $1/m$,

$$\|\eta_n\| \leq \frac{1}{m} [\|f - f_n\| + |F_{n-1}(0)| \|r_n\|].$$ (31)

If $z_0 = f$, the estimate simplifies to

$$\|\eta_n\| \leq \frac{\|r_n\|}{m}.$$ (31')

Instead of (31), a more simple estimate may be obtained which furnishes some idea of the speed of convergence of the process. From the variational problem, it follows that the quantity

$$(A\eta_n, \eta_n) = \left(\frac{P_n(A)}{P_n(0)}f, A^{-1}\frac{P_n(A)}{P_n(0)}f\right)$$ (32)

achieves its smallest value if $P_n(\lambda)$ is an orthogonal polynomial. In other words, if we were to substitute any other n-th degree polynomial in A in the formula (32) for $P_n(A)/P_n(0)$ normalized so that its constant term is unity, then the quantity $(A\eta_n, \eta_n)$ would be increased. Therefore,

$$(A\eta_n, \eta_n) \leqq (T_n(A)f, A^{-1}T_n(A)f),$$

where $T_n(\lambda)$ is the n-th Chebyshev polynomial (the polynomial deviating least from zero in the interval $[m, M]$) so normalized that $T_n(0) = 1$ (for even n). The resulting inequality can be simplified to

$$(A\eta_n, \eta_n) \leqq \frac{1}{m} \| T_n(A)f \|^2 \leqq \frac{L_n^2}{m} \|f\|^2,$$

where L_n is the maximum absolute value of $T_n(\lambda)$ in the interval $[m, M]$. Thus, we obtain

$$\| \eta_n \| \leqq \frac{L_n}{m} \|f\|. \tag{33}$$

It should be noted that the estimate (31) is more precise than (33).

We now proceed to consider operators that are not positive definite. We begin by treating self-adjoint operators having a spectrum with the property that on one side of the origin it consists of a finite number of eigenvalues which we let be $\lambda_1 < \lambda_2 < \ldots < \lambda_k < -\sigma$. Concerning the other side of the origin ($\lambda > 0$), nothing further is assumed.

From the fact that the sequence of spectral functions $\mathscr{E}_\lambda^{(n)}$ converges to $\mathscr{E}_\lambda$ and from the variational aspect of the problem, it follows that with increasing n, the k smallest roots of $P_n(\lambda)$ tend in a decreasing manner to the eigenvalues $\lambda_1, \lambda_2, \ldots, \lambda_k$.

Since none of the spectrum of A lies in the range $[-\sigma, \sigma]$, the function $(\mathscr{E}_\lambda z_0, z_0)$ is constant in this interval. By the third property of the orthogonal polynomials (see the end of §2), no more than one root of $P_n(\lambda)$ can lie in it which with increasing n will tend to $\lambda_k < -\sigma$. Hence, from some value of n onward, this root will lie outside the interval $[-\sigma, \sigma]$. Thus for such values of n, the approximate solution x_n of equation (24) will be given by (25):

$$x_n = \int_m^M \phi(\lambda) \, d\mathscr{E}_\lambda^{(n)} f = \int_m^M \frac{1}{\lambda} \, d\mathscr{E}_\lambda^{(n)} f = A_n^{-1} f_n.$$

It is easy to see that x_n also satisfies $A_n x_n = f_n$ in the present case and can be computed from formulas (27) or (27′).

Thus we have proved the following:

Theorem XI: *Let A be a bounded self-adjoint linear operator defined on the Hilbert space H and having a bounded inverse. If on one side of the origin, the spectrum of A consists of a finite number of eigenvalues and on the other side it is bounded, then beginning with some value of n, the x_n defined by (27) and (27′) exists and with increasing n the sequence $\{x_n\}$ converges strongly to the solution of equation (24) provided its right-hand side f is in the subspace H_z.*

The actual computation of an approximate solution by means of (27) or (27′) for the case of a self-adjoint operator is impractical since besides the terms in the orthogonal sequence p_k one also has to compute $z_k = A^k z_0$. As for the algorithm defined by (29) and (29′), it can be rejected if the operator is not positive definite since for certain values of n the approximate solution x_n need not exist $[P_n(0) = 0]$ which results in some of the coefficients h_n becoming infinite.

We now derive formulas that enable x_n to be expressed directly in terms of the orthogonal elements $p_0, p_1 \ldots$.

Since x_n belongs to H_n, it can be represented in the form

$$x_n = \sum_{k=0}^{n-1} \beta_k \, p_k.$$

Substituting this in

$$A_n x_n = f_n$$

and using the fact that

$$A_n p_k = p_{k+1} + a_k \, p_k + b_{k-1} \, p_{k-1},$$

$$A_n p_0 = p_1 + a_0 \, p_0,$$

$$A_n p_{n-1} = a_{n-1} \, p_{n-1} + b_{n-1} \, p_{n-1},$$

we obtain

$$\sum_{k=0}^{n-1} \beta_k (p_{k+1} + a_k \, p_k + b_{k-1} \, p_{k-1}) = f_n = \sum_{k=0}^{n-1} \frac{(f, p_k)}{\| p_k \|^2} \, p_k.$$

If we equate coefficients of like terms, this yields a system of equations for the coefficients β_k, namely,

$$\beta_{k-1} + a_k \beta_k + b_k \beta_{k+1} = \frac{(f, p_k)}{\| p_k \|^2}, \quad \beta_{-1} = \beta_n = 0. \tag{34}$$

This system is easily solved as follows. Setting $\beta_{n-1}^{(0)} = 1$, we compute quantities $\beta_k^{(0)}$ recursively from the formula

$$\beta_{k-1}^{(0)} = \frac{(f, p_k)}{\| p_k \|^2} - a_k \beta_k^{(0)} - b_k \beta_{k+1}^{(0)} \quad (k = n-1, \ldots, 0).$$

In so doing, we find, it is true, that $\beta^{(0)}_{-1}$ is not zero. Discarding the right-hand side of (34) and setting $\beta^{(1)}_{n-1} = 1$, we then find new quantities $\beta^{(1)}_k$ recursively from

$$\beta^{(1)}_{k-1} = -\alpha_k \beta^{(1)}_k - b_k \beta_k{}^{(1)}_{+1}.$$

$\beta^{(1)}_{-1} \neq 0$ if the approximate solution x_n exists which will always be the case according to Theorem X whenever n is sufficiently large. The difference

$$\beta_k = \beta^{(0)}_k - \frac{\beta^{(0)}_{-1}}{\beta^{(1)}_{-1}} \beta^{(1)}_k$$

furnishes the solution to the system (34).

If we choose $z_0 = p_0 = f$, the computations are considerably simplified. The system (34) becomes

$$\left. \begin{aligned} \beta_{k-1} + a_k \beta_k + b_k \beta_{k+1} &= 0 \quad (k = 1, 2, \ldots, n-1), \\ \beta_{-1} + a_0 \beta_0 + b_0 \beta_1 &= 1, \\ \beta_{-1} = \beta_n &= 0. \end{aligned} \right\} \tag{34'}$$

Setting $\beta^{(0)}_{n-1} = 1$, we compute $\beta^{(0)}_k$ from the formula

$$\beta^{(0)}_{k-1} = -a_k \beta^{(0)}_k - b_k \beta^{(0)}_{k+1}, \quad \beta^{(0)}_{-1} = -a_0 \beta^{(0)}_0 - b_0 \beta^{(0)}_1 + 1.$$

It is easy to see that the solution of the system (34') is given by

$$\beta_k = \beta^{(0)}_k \frac{1}{1 - \beta^{(0)}_{-1}} \quad (k = 0, 1, \ldots, n-1).$$

In the more general case of a bounded self-adjoint operator having an infinite number of points in its spectrum to the right and left of the origin, some of the roots of the orthogonal polynomials (the eigenvalues of the A_n) may possibly be equal to zero or arbitrarily close to zero for all n. The inverse operators A_n^{-1} may also not exist in H_n; however, if A^{-1} is bounded, the sequence $x_n = \phi(A_n)f_n$ will converge strongly as before to the solution of $Ax = f$. We represent f_n in the form of a sum $f_n = \bar{f}_n + \bar{g}_n$ where $\bar{f}_n$ is an element of the subspace $\bar{H}_n$ generated by the eigenelements of A_n corresponding to its eigenvalues lying outside the interval $[-\sigma, \sigma]$, and $\bar{g}_n$ is an element of the subspace of eigenelements of A_n corresponding to its eigenvalues lying inside $[-\sigma, \sigma]$. It is easy to see that

$$\phi(A_n)\bar{g}_n \Rightarrow 0.$$

In fact,

$$\| \phi(A_n)\bar{g}_n \| = \left\| \int_{-\sigma}^{+\sigma} \phi(\lambda)\, d\mathscr{E}_\lambda^{(n)}\bar{g}_n \right\| \leqq \max |\phi(\lambda)| \, \| (\mathscr{E}_\sigma^{(n)} - \mathscr{E}_{-\sigma}^{(n)})\bar{g}_n \| .$$

Since $\mathscr{E}_\sigma - \mathscr{E}_{-\sigma} = 0$ in consequence of the fact that none of the spectrum of A lies inside $[-\sigma, \sigma]$ and since $\mathscr{E}_\lambda^{(n)}$ tends to $\mathscr{E}_\lambda$, it follows that

$$\| (\mathscr{E}_\sigma^{(n)} - \mathscr{E}_{-\sigma}^{(n)})\bar{g}_n \| \to 0.$$

Thus we have shown that the sequence of elements $\bar{x}_n = \phi_n(A_n)\bar{f}_n = A_n^{-1}\bar{f}^n$ also converges strongly to the solution of equation (24). Note that the inverse operator A_n^{-1} always exists in the subspace $\bar{H}_n$ and its norm does not exceed $1/\sigma$.

Let us show how $\bar{x}_n$ may be computed. Let ξ_n be an eigenvalue of A_n lying in the interval $[-\sigma, \sigma]$. Represent $\bar{x}_n$ in the form

$$\bar{x}_n = A_n^{-1} [\bar{f}_n + C(A_n - \bar{\xi}^{(n)}I)^{-1}P_n(A_n)z_0].$$

Since $\bar{f}_n$ is an element of $\bar{H}_n$, it may be expressed in the polynomial form

$$\bar{f}_n = \bar{F}_{n-1}(A_n)z_0.$$

The constant C is chosen so as to satisfy the condition

$$\bar{F}_{n-1}(0) - C\frac{P_n(0)}{\bar{\xi}^{(n)}} = 0.$$

When this condition is satisfied, we may replace A_n in the expression for $\bar{x}_n$ by the operator A by virtue of formula (11) because it involves an $(n-1)$st degree polynomial in A_n.

This leads finally to the following expression for the approximate solution:

$$\bar{x}_n = A^{-1}\left[\bar{F}_{n-1}(A) + \frac{\bar{\xi}^{(n)}\bar{F}_{n-1}(0)}{P_n(0)}(A - \bar{\xi}^{(n)}I)^{-1}P_n(A)\right]z_0.$$

This formula should be used if one of the roots of $P_n(\lambda)$ falls in the interval $[-\sigma, \sigma]$. (No more than one can fall there.) If, however, all its roots lie outside $[-\sigma, \sigma]$, the approximate solution can be computed from the formulas described above.

An equation of the second kind,

$$x = Ax + f \tag{35}$$

may be solved by the same techniques.

If A is a self-adjoint and bounded operator, while $I-A$ is positive definite, which will be true, for example, if $\|A\| < 1$, the solution may be found by a procedure completely analogous to the algorithm (29):

$$x_{n+1} = x_n + F_n(1)h_n g_n, \tag{36}$$

$$g_n = r_n + l_{n-1}g_{n-1}, \qquad\qquad h_{n-1} = \frac{\|r_{n-1}\|^2}{(g_{n-1}-Ag_{n-1}, g_{n-1})},$$

$$r_n = r_{n-1} - h_{n-1}(g_{n-1}-Ag_{n-1}), \quad l_{n-1} = \frac{\|r_n\|^2}{\|r_{n-1}\|^2},$$

$$F_n(1) = F_{n-1}(1) + \frac{(f, r_n)}{\|r_n\|^2},$$

$$r_0 = g_0 = z_0, \quad F_0(1) = \frac{(f, z_0)}{\|z_0\|^2}.$$

Or, if we take $z_0 = f$,

$$x_{n+1} = x_n + h_n g_n, \tag{36'}$$

$$g_n = r_n + l_{n-1}g_{n-1}, \qquad\qquad h_{n-1} = \frac{\|r_{n-1}\|^2}{(g_{n-1}-Ag_{n-1}, g_{n-1})},$$

$$r_n = r_{n-1} - h_{n-1}(g_{n-1}-Ag_{n-1}), \quad l_{n-1} = \frac{\|r_n\|^2}{\|r_{n-1}\|^2},$$

$$r_0 = g_0 = f, \quad r_n = f - x_n + Ax_n.$$

However, if $I-A$ is not positive definite but satisfies the conditions of Theorem XI, an approximate solution to equation (35) can be obtained in the form

$$x_n = \sum_{k=0}^{n-1} \beta_k p_k.$$

Here, the β_k are determined from the system of equations

$$-\beta_{k-1} + (1-a_k)\beta_k - b_k\beta_{k+1} = \frac{(f, p_k)}{\|p_k\|^2}, \quad \beta_{-1} = \beta_n = 0, \tag{37}$$

whose solution can be found in the previous way.

Let us investigate the speed of convergence of the process under the assumption that A is self-adjoint and completely continuous. For simplicity, we confine our considerations to the most important case $z_0 = f$.

The approximate solution is given by

$$x_n = (I-A)^{-1}\left[I-\frac{P_n(A)}{P_n(1)}\right]f.$$

The right-hand side of this is an $(n-1)$st degree polynomial in A with a leading coefficient of $1/P_n(1)$. By virtue of the problem of moments, we have

$$Ax_n - A_n x_n = \frac{1}{P_n(1)}(A^n f - A_n^n f). \tag{38}$$

Since by definition of A_n, $A_n^n f$ is the projection of $A^n f$ on H_n, it follows that the inequality

$$\|A^n f - A_n^n f\| \le \|A^n f - Q_{n-1}(A)f\| \tag{39}$$

holds for any arbitrary polynomial $Q_{n-1}(\lambda)$. We choose $Q_{n-1}(\lambda)$ so that

$$\lambda^n - Q_{n-1}(\lambda) = (\lambda - \lambda_0)(\lambda - \lambda_1)\ldots(\lambda - \lambda_{n-1}),$$

where $\lambda_0, \ldots, \lambda_{n-1}$ are eigenvalues of A arranged in order of decreasing numerical value:

$$|\lambda_0| > |\lambda_1| > \ldots > |\lambda_n| > \ldots.$$

Recall that in the subspace H_z the spectrum of A is simple and all its eigenvalues are distinct.

If f is expanded in terms of the eigenelements of A:

$$f = \sum_{k=0}^{\infty} (f, u_k)u_k,$$

the inequality (39) then assumes the form

$$\|A^n f - A_n^n f\|^2 \le \sum_{k=0}^{\infty} [\lambda_k^n - Q_{n-1}(\lambda_k)]^2 (f, u_k)^2$$

$$= \sum_{k=n}^{\infty} (\lambda_k - \lambda_0)^2 \ldots (\lambda_k - \lambda_{n-1})^2 (f, u_k)^2$$

$$\le (|\lambda_0| + |\lambda_n|)^2 \ldots (|\lambda_{n-1}| + |\lambda_n|)^2 \sum_{k=n}^{\infty} (f, u_k)^2. \tag{40}$$

Now let η_n denote the error in the approximate solution x_n, so that $x = x_n + \eta_n$. Substitution in equation (34) yields

$$\eta_n - A\eta_n = Ax_n - x_n + f.$$

Since $x_n = A_n x_n + f$, by making use of equation (38), we conclude that

$$\eta_n - A\eta_n = Ax_n - A_n x_n = \frac{1}{P_n(1)}(A^n f - A_n^n f).$$

Finally, by means of (40), we arrive at the following estimate for the error in the approximate solution:

$$\| x - x_n \| = \| \eta_n \| \leqq \| (I - A)^{-1} \| (|\lambda_0| + |\lambda_n|) \ldots$$

$$\ldots (|\lambda_{n-1}| + |\lambda_n|) \frac{1}{|P_n(1)|} \sqrt{\left(\sum_{k=n}^{\infty} (f, u_k)^2 \right)}$$

$$= \| (I - A)^{-1} \| \frac{|\lambda_0| + |\lambda_n|}{|1 - \lambda_0^{(n)}|} \cdots \frac{|\lambda_{n-1}| + |\lambda_n|}{|1 - \lambda_{n-1}^{(n)}|} \sqrt{\left(\sum_{k=n}^{\infty} (f, u_k)^2 \right)},$$

$$(41)$$

where $\lambda_0^{(n)}, \ldots, \lambda_{n-1}^{(n)}$ are the eigenvalues of A_n. When n approaches infinity, $\lambda_k^{(n)} \to \lambda_k$ and $|\lambda_n| \to 0$, and therefore x_n tends to x faster than any geometric progression.

Despite the fact the process converges fairly rapidly to the solution, it may prove more reasonable to use the method of moments in combination with some simple iterative process if the eigenvalues of the given operator decrease slowly.

CHAPTER IV

Speeding Up the Convergence of Linear Iterative Processes

I. Linear Iterative Processes

The classical Liouville-Neumann method of solving a non-homogeneous linear equation

$$x = Ax + f \tag{1}$$

proceeds as follows. Given an arbitrary element x_0, one finds successive approximations by means of the formula

$$x_{n+1} = Ax_n + f.$$

The iterations converge by Theorem V (Banach's Theorem) to the solution of (1) when $\|A\| < 1$. The shortcomings of the method are twofold. First, the range of problems to which it may be applied is limited because of the imposition of the very stringent convergence condition, $\|A\| < 1$. Second, even in those problems where the process does converge, it often turns out that on account of its slow rate of convergence, one has to compute a great number of approximations to actually obtain the solution to a satisfactory degree of accuracy. In this connection, a variety of methods have been developed in recent years for speeding up the convergence of iterative processes that has resulted both in a broadening of the class of problems solvable by iterations and in a reduction in the number of computations.

The methods for speeding up the convergence of iterative processes can be classified into two types. In the first type, the given equation (1) is replaced by an equivalent one

$$x = P(A)x + Q(A)f,$$

in which $P(\lambda)$ and $Q(\lambda)$ are polynomials with $Q(\lambda) = [1 - P(\lambda)]/(1 - \lambda)$ and $P(1) = 1$. The polynomial $P(\lambda)$ is so chosen that the norm of the operator $P(A)$ is as small as possible. For a self-adjoint operator, the norm of $P(A)$ may be estimated by means of the relation

$$P(A)x = \int_m^M P(\lambda)\, d\mathscr{E}_\lambda x.$$

If $|P(\lambda)|$ does not exceed q in the interval $[m, M]$, then

$$\| P(A) \| \leq q.$$

Therefore, M. Gavurin [1] and G. Shortley [1] have suggested the use of Chebyshev polynomials which deviate least from zero in the interval $[m, M]$ containing the entire spectrum of an operator.

To the second type belong methods which do not alter the given equation but make direct use of a number of the successive approximations to find the solution. The idea underlying such methods is due to L. Lyusternik [1].

In applying these methods, one begins with the following considerations. The equation (1) is solved by the method of successive approximations,

$$x_{k+1} = Ax_k + f.$$

For the sake of simplicity, A will be assumed to be self-adjoint and completely continuous. The error in the k-th approximation, $\eta_k = x - x_k$, is expressible as

$$\eta_k = A^k \eta_0.$$

Therefore, if we expand η_0 in terms of the eigenelements of A,

$$\eta_0 = \sum_{s=0}^{\infty} a_s u_s,$$

we have

$$\eta_k = \sum_{s=0}^{\infty} \lambda_s^k a_s u_s.$$

As the number of iterations is increased, the terms corresponding to the numerically small eigenvalues decrease rapidly and for sufficiently large k

$$\left\| \sum_{s=n}^{\infty} \lambda_s^k a_s u_s \right\| \leq |\lambda_n|^k \sqrt{\left(\sum_{s=n}^{\infty} a_s^2 \right)} \approx 0.$$

Hence,

$$\eta_k \approx \sum_{s=0}^{n-1} \lambda_s^k a_s u_s,$$

where $\lambda_0, \lambda_1, \ldots, \lambda_{n-1}$ are the n numerically largest eigenvalues.

A similar fact also holds for the corrections $\varepsilon_k = x_{k+1} - x_k$. Namely,

$$\varepsilon_k = A^k \varepsilon_0,$$

and for sufficiently large k,

$$\varepsilon_k = \sum_{s=0}^{n-1} \lambda_s^k (\varepsilon_0, u_s) u_s.$$

Here, we have assumed that

$$\left\| \sum_{s=n}^{\infty} \lambda_s^k (\varepsilon_0, u_s) u_s \right\| \leq |\lambda_n|^k \sqrt{\left(\sum_{s=n}^{\infty} (\varepsilon_0, u_s)^2 \right)} \approx 0.$$

Suppose now that the n-th degree equation

$$G(\lambda) = \sum_{k=1}^{n} \alpha_k \lambda^k = 0 \quad (\alpha_0 = 1)$$

has as its roots the n numerically largest eigenvalues $\lambda_0, \lambda_1, \ldots, \lambda_{n-1}$. Then

$$\sum_{k=1}^{n} \alpha_k \varepsilon_k \approx \sum_{s=0}^{n-1} G(\lambda_s)(\varepsilon_0, u_s) u_s = 0$$

and from the system of linear equations

$$\sum_{k=1}^{n} \alpha_k \varepsilon_k = 0$$

the coefficients α_k are found in one way or another.

The required solution can now easily be determined. For,

$$\sum_{k=1}^{n} \alpha_k \eta_k \approx \sum_{s=0}^{n-1} G(\lambda_s) a_s u_s = 0,$$

or

$$\sum_{k=1}^{n} \alpha_k (x_* - x_k) \approx 0.$$

Hence

$$x \approx \frac{\sum_{k=1}^{n} \alpha_k x_k}{G(1)}.$$

This way of speeding up the convergence of the iterations is sometimes called the *extrapolation* method.

2. The Method of Moments and Speeding up the Convergence of Linear Iterative Processes

We again consider the equation

$$x = Ax + f, \tag{1}$$

and we solve it by the usual iterative scheme. We define successive approximations by

$$x_{k+1} = Ax_k + f.$$

The initial approximation x_0 is arbitrary.

The approximative process can be handled more satisfactorily if instead of the approximations themselves one calculates the corrections to them. Let

$$x_{k+1} = x_k + \varepsilon_k,$$

and consider two successive approximations

$$x_k = Ax_{k-1} + f, \quad x_{k+1} = Ax_k + f.$$

Subtraction of the two approximations yields

$$\varepsilon_k = A\varepsilon_{k-1}.$$

Thus, when we use the above iterative process, we are actually computing a sequence of iterations of ε_0 by means of the operator A. Suppose $l+n$ such iterations have been performed. Then x_{l+n} is given by

$$x_{l+n} = x_0 + \varepsilon_0 + \ldots + \varepsilon_{l-1} + \varepsilon_l + \ldots + \varepsilon_{l+n-1}.$$

In the application of the method, the following question arises: Could one not obtain a far more exact solution if instead of simply adding the successive corrections, one first multiplied them by suitably chosen coefficients and sought an approximate solution of the form

$$x_l^{(n)} = x_0 + \varepsilon_0 + \ldots + \varepsilon_{l-1} + a_0 \varepsilon_l + \ldots + a_{n-1} \varepsilon_{l+n-1}? \tag{2}$$

Let us show how the method of moments can in fact be used to calculate the coefficients a_j.

Let η_l denote the error in the l-th approximation:

$$x_* = x_l + \eta_l,$$

with x_* the required solution of equation (1). The substitution of this in (1) yields

$$x_l + \eta_l = A x_l + A \eta_l + f = x_{l+1} + A \eta_l,$$

$$\eta_l = A \eta_l + \varepsilon_l. \tag{3}$$

We next solve this equation for the error approximately by the method of moments replacing A by the approximate operator A_n such that

$$\varepsilon_{l+k} = A_n \varepsilon_{l+k-1} \quad (k = 0, 1, \ldots, n-1),$$

$$E_n \varepsilon_{l+n} = A_n \varepsilon_{l+n-1}.$$

Here, E_n is the operator projecting onto the subspace H_n generated by all linear combinations of $\varepsilon_l, \varepsilon_{l+1}, \ldots, \varepsilon_{l+n-1}$. By solving the equation

$$\eta_l^{(n)} = A_n \eta_l^{(n)} + \varepsilon_l, \tag{4}$$

we find an approximate solution to (1) given by

$$x_l^{(n)} = x_l + \eta_l^{(n)}.$$

It is easy to see that $x_l^{(n)}$ has exactly the form (2) (Cf. the end of §4, Chapter III).

We give the results for $n = 1$ and $n = 2$.

(1) $n = 1$:

$$\eta_l^{(1)} = (I - A)^{-1} \left[I - \frac{A + \alpha_0 I}{1 + \alpha_0} \right] \varepsilon_l = \frac{\varepsilon_l}{1 + \alpha_0}.$$

The coefficient α_0 is determined from the system (11) of Chapter I:

$$\alpha_0 = - \frac{(\varepsilon_l, \varepsilon_{l+1})}{(\varepsilon_l, \varepsilon_l)}.$$

$$x_l^{(1)} = x_l - \frac{(\varepsilon_l, \varepsilon_l)}{(\varepsilon_l, \varepsilon_{l+1}) - (\varepsilon_l, \varepsilon_l)} \varepsilon_l.$$

(2) $n = 2$:

$$\eta_l^{(2)} = (I - A)^{-1} \left[I - \frac{A^2 + \alpha_1 A + \alpha_0 I}{1 + \alpha_1 + \alpha_0} \right] \varepsilon_l$$

$$= \frac{1}{1 + \alpha_1 + \alpha_0} \left[A + (1 + \alpha_1) I \right] \varepsilon_l,$$

with α_0 and α_1 the solution of the system

$$(\varepsilon_l, \varepsilon_l)\alpha_0 + (\varepsilon_l, \varepsilon_{l+1})\alpha_1 + (\varepsilon_l, \varepsilon_{l+2}) = 0,$$

$$(\varepsilon_{l+1}, \varepsilon_l)\alpha_0 + (\varepsilon_{l+1}, \varepsilon_{l+1})\alpha_1 + (\varepsilon_{l+1}, \varepsilon_{l+2}) = 0.$$

Finally,

$$x_l^{(2)} = x_l + \frac{1+\alpha_1}{1+\alpha_1+\alpha_0}\varepsilon_l + \frac{1}{1+\alpha_1+\alpha_0}\varepsilon_{l+1}.$$

This way of computing the quantities $\eta_l^{(n)}$ can turn out to be very inefficient for large values of n on account of the great loss of accuracy in calculating α_k. Therefore, it is necessary to resort to complete or partial orthogonalization of the sequence of corrections ε_k. To this end, we take any subspace R_m of dimension $m \geqq n$ in the given space H such that the projections of $\varepsilon_l, \varepsilon_{l+1}, \ldots, \varepsilon_{l+n-1}$ on R_m are linearly independent. In particular, R_m may be H. We orthogonalize the projections of $\varepsilon_l, \ldots, \varepsilon_{l+n-1}$ on the subspace R_m by setting

$$g_0 = \varepsilon_l, \qquad\qquad c_0^{(1)} = \frac{(P_m A g_0, P_m g_0)}{(P_m g_0, P_m g_0)}$$

$$g_1 = A g_0 - c_0^{(1)} g_0, \qquad\qquad c_k^{(n-1)} = \frac{(P_m A g_{n-2}, P_m g_k)}{(P_m g_k, P_m g_k)},$$

$$\cdot \quad \cdot \quad \cdot \quad \cdot \quad \cdot \quad \cdot$$

$$g_{n-1} = A g_{n-2} - \sum_{k=0}^{n-2} c_k^{(n-1)} g_k,$$

where P_m is the operator projecting onto R_m. It is usually expedient to take R_m to be the subspace defined by m coordinate elements since this greatly simplifies the computation of scalar products.

If we write

$$\eta_l^{(n)} = b_0 g_0 + b_1 g_1 + \ldots + b_{n-1} g_{n-1}$$

and substitute this in equation (4), we obtain a system of linear equations for the coefficients b_k:

$$\sum_{k=0}^{n-1} b_k(g_k, g_s) = \sum_{k=0}^{n-1} b_k(A g_k, g_s) + (g_0, g_s) \quad (s = 0, 1, \ldots, n-1).$$

The inequality (41) of Chapter III can be applied to estimate the speed of convergence of the process when A is self-adjoint and completely continuous. We have

$$\| x_* - x_l^{(n)} \| \leq \| (I-A)^{-1} \| \frac{|\lambda_0| + |\lambda_n|}{|1 - \lambda_0^{(n)}|} \cdots$$

$$\cdots \frac{|\lambda_{n-1}| + |\lambda_n|}{|1 - \lambda_{n-1}^{(n)}|} \sqrt{\left(\sum_{k=n}^{\infty} (\varepsilon_l, u_k)^2 \right)}.$$

Since $\qquad \varepsilon_l = A^l \varepsilon_0, \quad (\varepsilon_l, u_k) = \lambda_k^l (\varepsilon_0, u_k),$

this leads to

$$\| x_* - x_l^{(n)} \| \leq \| (I-A)^{-1} \| \frac{|\lambda_0| + |\lambda_n|}{|1 - \lambda_0^{(n)}|} \cdots$$

$$\cdots \frac{|\lambda_{n-1}| + |\lambda_n|}{|1 - \lambda_{n-1}^{(n)}|} |\lambda_n|^l \sqrt{\left(\sum_{k=n}^{\infty} (\varepsilon_0, u_k)^2 \right)}. \quad (5)$$

Thus, for fixed n, the process converges at least as fast as a geometric progression with ratio $|\lambda_n|$, whereas we know the ordinary iterative process can be estimated by a geometric progression having a ratio $|\lambda_0|$. Recall that the complete continuity of an operator implies that $|\lambda_n| \to 0$ when n tends to infinity.

It also should be noted that for $|\lambda_0| > 1$, the simple iterative process diverges, whereas for sufficiently large n, the process described above converges to the solution of equation (1).

Another way of speeding up the convergence of an iterative process by use of the method of moments was discussed for the Liouville-Neumann method in the chapter on completely continuous operators. A procedure was given there for transforming (1) into a form enabling its solution to be found by means of the Liouville-Neumann method.

If the method of moments is applied under the conditions of the extrapolation method, the sum under the radical on the right-hand side of the inequality (5) is exactly the quantity that was assumed to be arbitrarily small, and therefore

$$x_k^{(n)} \approx x_*.$$

Thus, in the considered case, the order of the error in the approximations is roughly the same in both methods. However, the method of moments has a number of important advantages:

(1) The admissible error in the extrapolation method cannot be estimated because the spectrum of the operator is not known. Thus, if

an attempt is undertaken prematurely to speed up the convergence, this may actually lead to a worsening instead of an improvement in the approximate solution. This cannot happen in the method of moments whose convergence has been established under very general assumptions. Moreover, we can always effectively estimate the accuracy achieved by the method.

(2) The method of moments can be successfully applied to speed up the convergence of an iterative process where the usual method is either generally not applicable or is impractical. This certainly holds for certain non-self-adjoint operators or if the eigenvalues are densely packed and singling out several of the largest ones is meaningless. However, this fact is of no significance for the method of moments since it may be used even in the limiting case where the operator has a continuous spectrum.

It should be noted that the last property is especially important in the solution of finite difference equations with fine mesh for which the eigenvalues lie very close to one another and where the spectrum becomes continuous in the limit when the mesh width is allowed to approach zero.

3. Solution of Finite Difference Equations

Consider a boundary value problem of the first kind defined by the elliptic equation

$$a\frac{\partial^2 u}{\partial x^2} + b\frac{\partial^2 u}{\partial y^2} + c\frac{\partial u}{\partial x} + d\frac{\partial u}{\partial y} - gu = f(x, y), \tag{6}$$

with a, b, c, d and g constants such that $a > 0$, $b > 0$, and $g \geqq 0$. On the boundary Γ of the region, the function $u(x,y)$ is prescribed as

$$u\mid_\Gamma = \phi(s).$$

Numerical methods for solving (6) lead to a system of linear equations. Using a square mesh and replacing the derivatives in (6) by finite differences, we obtain

$$\left(a + \frac{h}{2}c\right)u_{i+1,k} + \left(a - \frac{h}{2}c\right)u_{i-1,k} + \left(b + \frac{h}{2}d\right)u_{i,k+1}$$

$$+ \left(b - \frac{h}{2}d\right)u_{i,k-1} - (2a + 2b + h^2 g)u_{i,k} = h^2 f_{i,k}, \tag{7}$$

where $u_{i,k}$ and $f_{i,k}$ are the values of $u(x,y)$ and $f(x,y)$ at the mesh points, and h is the mesh width. For simplicity, assume that the points on the periphery of the mesh lie on Γ. The determinant of the system (7) is different from zero and therefore these equations always have a solution. Thus, one would think that the problem is completely solved. To obtain the values of $u(x,y)$ at the mesh points, one would merely have to solve the system of linear algebraic equations using Cramer's rule. However, in order to obtain values of the unknown function $u(x,y)$ to a satisfactory degree of accuracy, it might be necessary to use a mesh of fairly small width and thus involve several hundred mesh points. The solution of the resulting system by "exact" algebraic methods is impracticable. Therefore the question of solving finite difference equations efficiently becomes one of fundamental importance.

Today, finite difference equations are solved exclusively by successive approximation procedures, but they all have the same essential defects. As the size of the mesh width is decreased so as to reduce the error resulting from replacing the differential equation by a finite difference equation, not only is there an increase in the number of points at which the potential has to be determined but there is also a sharp drop in the speed of convergence of the successive approximations. Moreover, generally speaking, when the mesh width tends to zero, the successive approximation procedures all fail to converge. This is due to the fact that when the mesh width approaches zero, the determinant of the system of finite difference equations also tends to zero.

An analysis of finite difference operators carried out in a paper by L. Lyusternik [3] shows that the more exact the finite difference equation, the faster is the convergence of the iterative process. The use of such an equation permits one to approximate a differential equation with considerable accuracy using a mesh of fairly large width. Unfortunately, the matter is complicated by the fact that to satisfy the boundary condition, one often has to use a refined mesh of mild width close to the boundary since no refinement of the finite difference formulas can take into account all the characteristics of both the values of the unknown function along the boundary and the boundary itself.

Let us begin solving the system of equations (7). We assume that the periphery points of the mesh lie on the boundary of the region on which the value of $u(x,y)$ is prescribed. We start with an approximate solution $u^{(0)}$ which may be chosen arbitrarily. Let u^* be the required solution. Then if

$$u^* = u^{(0)} + \eta,$$

the error η satisfies the equation

$$\left(a+\frac{h}{2}c\right)\eta_{i+1,k}+\left(a-\frac{h}{2}c\right)\eta_{i-1,k}+\left(b+\frac{h}{2}d\right)\eta_{i,k+1}$$

$$+\left(b-\frac{h}{2}d\right)\eta_{i,k-1}-(2a+2b+h^2g)\eta_{i,k}=-q_{i,k}, \quad (8)$$

with

$$q_{i,k}=-h^2f_{i,k}+\left(a+\frac{h}{2}c\right)u^{(0)}_{i+1,k}+\left(a-\frac{h}{2}c\right)u^{(0)}_{i-1,k}$$

$$+\left(b+\frac{h}{2}d\right)u^{(0)}_{i,k+1}+\left(b-\frac{h}{2}d\right)u^{(0)}_{i,k-1}-(2a+2b+h^2g)u^{(0)}_{i,k},$$

and $\eta_{i,k}=0$ at the periphery points of the mesh.

To solve the equations (8), we eliminate half the unknowns. If we choose the points in staggered fashion (Fig. 1) and eliminate $\eta_{i,k+1}$, $\eta_{i,k-1}$, $\eta_{i+1,k}$, and $\eta_{i-1,k}$ from (8), we arrive at

$$\eta_{i,k}=\frac{1}{(2a+2b+h^2g)^2-2(a^2+b^2)+\dfrac{h^2}{2}(c^2+d^2)}$$

$$\times\left\{\left(a+\frac{h}{2}c\right)^2\eta_{i+2,k}+\left(a-\frac{h}{2}c\right)^2\eta_{i-2,k}\right.$$

$$+\left(b+\frac{h}{2}d\right)^2\eta_{i,k+2}+\left(b-\frac{h}{2}d\right)^2\eta_{i,k-2}$$

$$+2\left(a+\frac{h}{2}c\right)\left(b+\frac{h}{2}d\right)\eta_{i+1,k+1}$$

$$+2\left(a-\frac{h}{2}c\right)\left(b+\frac{h}{2}d\right)\eta_{i-1,k+1}$$

$$+2\left(a+\frac{h}{2}c\right)\left(b-\frac{h}{2}d\right)\eta_{i+1,k-1}$$

$$+2\left(a-\frac{h}{2}c\right)\left(b-\frac{h}{2}d\right)\eta_{i-1,k-1}$$

$$+\left(a+\frac{h}{2}c\right)q_{i+1,k}+\left(a-\frac{h}{2}c\right)q_{i-1,k}$$

$$+\left.\left(b+\frac{h}{2}d\right)q_{i,k+1}+\left(b-\frac{h}{2}d\right)q_{i,k-1}+(2a+2b+h^2g)q_{i,k}\right\}. \quad (9)$$

These equations relate the unknowns at the points indicated in Fig. 1 by the black dots.

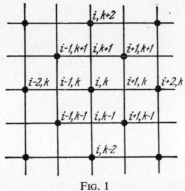

FIG. 1

The equations are slightly different at points adjacent to the boundary of the region. For example, if the point $i-1,k$ lies on the boundary (Fig. 2) and hence $\eta_{i-1,k}=0$, the elimination of $\eta_{i,k+1}$, $\eta_{i+1,k}$, and $\eta_{i,k-1}$ from (8) yields

$$\eta_{i,k} = \frac{1}{(2a+2b+h^2g)^2 - a^2 - 2b^2 + \dfrac{h^2}{4}(c^2+2d^2)}$$

$$\times \left\{ \left(a+\frac{h}{2}c\right)^2 \eta_{i+2,k} + \left(b+\frac{h}{2}d\right)^2 \eta_{i,k+2} \right.$$

$$+ \left(b-\frac{h}{2}d\right)^2 \eta_{i,k-2} + 2\left(a+\frac{h}{2}c\right)\left(b+\frac{h}{2}d\right)\eta_{i+1,k+1}$$

$$+ 2\left(a+\frac{h}{2}c\right)\left(b-\frac{h}{2}d\right)\eta_{i+1,k-1}$$

$$+ \left(a-\frac{h}{2}c\right)\left(b+\frac{h}{2}d\right)\eta_{i-1,k+1}$$

$$+ \left(a-\frac{h}{2}c\right)\left(b-\frac{h}{2}d\right)\eta_{i-1,k-1}$$

$$+ \left(a+\frac{h}{2}c\right)q_{i+1,k} + \left(b+\frac{h}{2}d\right)q_{i,k+1}$$

$$\left. + \left(b-\frac{h}{2}d\right)q_{i,k-1} + (2a+2b+h^2g)q_{i,k} \right\}. \quad (9')$$

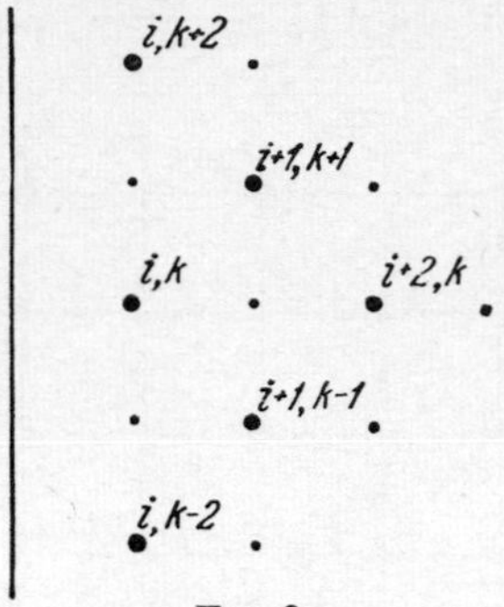

Fig. 2

However, if two neighboring points lie on the boundary, say, both $i-1,k$ and $i,k+1$ (Fig. 3), then $\eta_{i-1,k}=\eta_{i,k+1}=0$ and the equation becomes

$$\eta_{i,k}=\frac{1}{(2a+2b+h^2g)^2-a^2-b^2+\dfrac{h^2}{4}(c^2+d^2)}$$

$$\times\left\{\left(a+\frac{h}{2}c\right)^2\eta_{i+2,k}+\left(b-\frac{h}{2}c\right)^2\eta_{i,k-2}\right.$$

$$+2\left(a+\frac{h}{2}c\right)\left(b-\frac{h}{2}d\right)\eta_{i+1,k-1}$$

$$+\left(a+\frac{h}{2}c\right)\left(b-\frac{h}{2}d\right)\eta_{i+1,k+1}$$

$$+\left(a-\frac{h}{2}c\right)\left(b-\frac{h}{2}d\right)\eta_{i-1,k-1}+\left(a+\frac{h}{2}c\right)q_{i+1,k}$$

$$\left.+\left(b-\frac{h}{2}d\right)q_{i,k-1}+(2a+2b+h^2g)q_{i,k}\right\}. \qquad (9'')$$

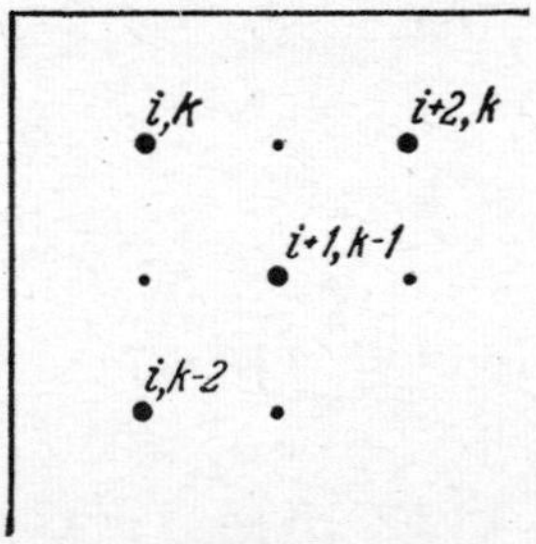

Fig. 3

The elimination of the unknowns achieves two purposes. First, the iterations converge considerably faster in the solution of equations (9) than for equations (8). Second, the halving of the number of unknowns simplifies the work in computing scalar products required in the method of moments.

It is convenient to solve the equations (9) by the method of moments in conjunction with the Seidel iterative method in which successive corrections are determined by means of the formulas

$$\varepsilon_{i,k}^{(s+1)} = \frac{1}{(2a+2b+h^2g)^2 - 2(a^2+b^2) + \dfrac{h^2}{2}(c^2+d^2)}$$

$$\times \left\{ \left(a+\frac{h}{2}c\right)^2 \varepsilon_{i+2,k}^{(s)} + \left(a-\frac{h}{2}c\right)^2 \varepsilon_{i-2,k}^{(s+1)} \right.$$

$$+ \left(b+\frac{h}{2}d\right)^2 \varepsilon_{i,k+2}^{(s+1)} + \left(b-\frac{h}{2}d\right)^2 \varepsilon_{i,k-2}^{(s)}$$

$$+ 2\left(a+\frac{h}{2}c\right)\left(b+\frac{h}{2}d\right)\varepsilon_{i+1,k+1}^{(s+1)}$$

$$+ 2\left(a-\frac{h}{2}c\right)\left(b+\frac{h}{2}d\right)\varepsilon_{i-1,k+1}^{(s+1)}$$

$$\left. + 2\left(a+\frac{h}{2}c\right)\left(b-\frac{h}{2}d\right)\varepsilon_{i+1,k-1}^{(s)} + 2\left(a-\frac{h}{2}c\right)\left(b-\frac{h}{2}d\right)\varepsilon_{i-1,k-1}^{(s)} \right\},$$

$$\varepsilon_{i,k}^{(0)} = \frac{1}{(2a+2b+h^2g)^2 - 2(a^2+b^2) + \dfrac{h^2}{2}(c^2+d^2)}$$

$$\times \left\{ \left(a-\frac{h}{2}c\right)\varepsilon_{i-2,k}^{(0)} + \left(b+\frac{h}{2}d\right)\varepsilon_{i,k+2}^{(0)} \right.$$

$$+ 2\left(a+\frac{h}{2}c\right)\left(b+\frac{h}{2}d\right)\varepsilon_{i+1,k+1}^{(0)}$$

$$+ 2\left(a-\frac{h}{2}c\right)\left(b+\frac{h}{2}d\right)\varepsilon_{i-1,k+1}^{(0)} + \left(a+\frac{h}{2}c\right)q_{i+1,k}$$

$$+ \left(a-\frac{h}{2}c\right)q_{i-1,k} + \left(b+\frac{h}{2}d\right)q_{i,k+1}$$

$$\left. + \left(b-\frac{h}{2}d\right)q_{i,k-1} + (2a+2b+h^2g)q_{i,k} \right\}.$$

Computing $\varepsilon^{(s)}$ is equivalent to computing successive iterations of $\varepsilon^{(0)}$ by the use of a linear operator A:

$$\varepsilon^{(s)} = A\varepsilon^{(s-1)}.$$

Therefore, an approximate solution of (9) may be found by the method of moments of the form

$$\eta = \varepsilon^{(0)} + \varepsilon^{(1)} + \ldots + \varepsilon^{(l-1)} + (I-A)^{-1}\left[I - \frac{P_n(A)}{P_n(1)}\right]\varepsilon^{(l)}, \qquad (10)$$

with the coefficients of the polynomial $P_n(\lambda) = \lambda^n + \alpha_{n-1}\lambda^{n-1} + \ldots + \alpha_0$ determined from the system of linear equations,

$$\left.\begin{array}{l} (\varepsilon^{(l)}, \varepsilon^{(l)})\alpha_0 + \ldots + (\varepsilon^{(l)}, \varepsilon^{(l+n-1)})\alpha_{n-1} + (\varepsilon^{(l)}, \varepsilon^{(l+n)}) = 0, \\ \cdot \quad \cdot \\ (\varepsilon^{(l+n-1)}, \varepsilon^{(l)})\alpha_0 + \ldots + (\varepsilon^{(l+n-1)}, \varepsilon^{(l+n-1)})\alpha_{n-1} + (\varepsilon^{(l+n-1)}, \varepsilon^{(l+n)}) = 0. \end{array}\right\}$$

The scalar product here is understood to be the quantity

$$(\varepsilon^{(l)}, \varepsilon^{(l+j)}) = \sum_{i,k} \varepsilon_{i,k}^{(l)}\varepsilon_{i,k}^{(l+j)},$$

the summation extending over all interior points of the mesh indicated by the dots in Fig. 1.

Thus, for example, for $n = 1$,

$$\eta = \varepsilon^{(0)} + \ldots + \varepsilon^{(l+1)} + \frac{(\varepsilon^{(l)}, \varepsilon^{(l)})}{(\varepsilon^{(l)}, \varepsilon^{(l)}) - (\varepsilon^{(l)}, \varepsilon^{(l+1)})}\varepsilon^{(l)},$$

while for $n = 2$,

$$\eta = \varepsilon^{(0)} + \ldots + \varepsilon^{(l+1)} + \frac{1+\alpha_1}{1+\alpha_1+\alpha_0}\varepsilon^{(l)} + \frac{1}{1+\alpha_1+\alpha_0}\varepsilon^{(l+1)},$$

$$\left.\begin{array}{l} (\varepsilon^{(l)}, \varepsilon^{(l)})\alpha_0 + (\varepsilon^{(l)}, \varepsilon^{(l+1)})\alpha_1 + (\varepsilon^{(l)}, \varepsilon^{(l+2)}) = 0 \\ (\varepsilon^{(l+1)}, \varepsilon^{(l)})\alpha_0 + (\varepsilon^{(l+1)}, \varepsilon^{(l+1)})\alpha_1 + (\varepsilon^{(l+1)}, \varepsilon^{(l+2)}) = 0. \end{array}\right\}$$

For large values of n, it is necessary to orthogonalize the corrections $\varepsilon^{(l+k)}$ in the manner indicated above.

Generally speaking, only an approximate solution results which if necessary can again be refined by applying the Seidel method.

After $u_{i,k} = u_{i,k}^{(0)} + \eta_i$ has been calculated at the points of the mesh indicated by dots, the values of $u_{i,k}$ at the remaining points can be computed immediately from (7).

As an illustration, we consider the two-dimensional Dirichlet problem for a square with the data of Fig. 4.

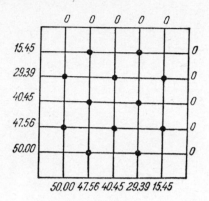

FIG. 4

The finite difference equations become

$$u_{i,k+1} + u_{i+1,k} + u_{i,k-1} + u_{i-1,k} - 4u_{i,k} = 0, \tag{7}$$

$$\left.\begin{array}{l} \eta_{i+1,k} + \eta_{i-1,k} + \eta_{i,k+1} + \eta_{i,k-1} - 4\eta_{i,k} = -q_{i,k}, \\ q_{i,k} = u^{(0)}_{i,k+1} + u^{(0)}_{i-1,k} + u^{(0)}_{i+1,k} + u^{(0)}_{i,k-1} - 4u^{(0)}_{i,k}, \end{array}\right\} \tag{8}$$

$$\eta_{i,k} = \tfrac{1}{6}(\eta_{i+1,k+1} + \eta_{i-1,k+1} + \eta_{i-1,k-1} + \eta_{i+1,k-1})$$
$$+ \tfrac{1}{12}(\eta_{i,k+2} + \eta_{i,k-2} + \eta_{i+2,k} + \eta_{i-2,k}) + \tfrac{1}{3}q_{i,k}$$
$$+ \tfrac{1}{12}(q_{i,k+1} + q_{i,k-1} + q_{i+1,k} + q_{i-1,k}), \tag{9}$$

$$\eta_{i,k} = \tfrac{1}{13}\left[2(\eta_{i+1,k+1} + \eta_{i+1,k-1}) + \eta_{i-1,k+1} + \eta_{i-1,k-1}\right.$$
$$\left. + \eta_{i,k+2} + \eta_{i+2,k} + \eta_{i,k-2}\right]$$
$$+ \tfrac{1}{13}(4q_{i,k} + q_{i,k+1} + q_{i+1,k} + q_{i,k-1}), \tag{9'}$$

$$\eta_{i,k} = \tfrac{1}{14}\left[2\eta_{i+1,k-1} + \eta_{i+1,k+1} + \eta_{i-1,k-1}\right.$$
$$\left. + \eta_{i+2,k} + \eta_{i,k-2}\right] + \tfrac{1}{14}(4q_{i,k} + q_{i+1,k} + q_{i,k-1}). \tag{9''}$$

An initial approximation $u^{(0)}$ is given by

			$u^{(0)}$			
	0.00	0.00	0.00	0.00	0.00	
15.45	12.88	10.30	7.72	5.15	2.58	0.00
29.39	24.54	19.69	14.85	10.00	5.15	0.00
40.45	34.05	27.65	21.25	14.85	7.72	0.00
47.56	40.92	34.29	27.65	19.69	10.30	0.00
50.00	45.46	40.92	34.05	24.54	12.88	0.00
	50.00	47.56	40.45	29.39	15.45	

Continuation

		$q_{i,\,k}$		
− 123	− 91	− 58	− 30	− 2
− 215	− 142	− 74	0	− 30
− 264	− 132	0	− 74	− 58
− 232	− 2	− 132	− 142	− 91
0	− 232	− 264	− 215	− 123

(The values in the above second table and in the two that follow have been suitably normalized).

The first few successive corrections $\varepsilon_{i,k}^{(s)}$ are tabulated below:

$\varepsilon^{(0)}$		$\varepsilon^{(1)}$		$\varepsilon^{(2)}$	
− 69	− 42	− 34	− 21	− 18	− 11
− 107	− 94	− 45	− 52	− 23	− 28
− 127		− 67		− 36	
− 100		− 48		− 25	

Those below the diagonal follow from the symmetry of the solution.

The corresponding scalar products are

$$(\varepsilon^{(0)}, \varepsilon^{(0)}) = 52\,939, \quad (\varepsilon_0, \varepsilon_1) = 26\,240, \quad (\varepsilon_0, \varepsilon_2) = 13\,869,$$
$$(\varepsilon_1, \varepsilon_1) = 13\,119, \quad (\varepsilon_1, \varepsilon_2) = 6946.$$

Solving the equations

$$52\,939\alpha_0 + 26\,240\alpha_1 + 13\,869 = 0,$$
$$26\,240\alpha_0 + 13\,119\alpha_1 + 6946 = 0,$$

we find that $\alpha_1 = -0.635$ and $\alpha_0 = 0.053$.

Thus, the approximate value of the error is given by (for $l = 0$, $n = 2$)

$$\eta = \frac{1+\alpha_1}{1+\alpha_1+\alpha_0}\varepsilon^{(0)} + \frac{1}{1+\alpha_1+\alpha_0}\varepsilon^{(1)} = 0.874\varepsilon^{(0)} + 2.39\varepsilon^{(1)}$$

$$\eta$$

	-143		-87
-202		-206	
	-271		
-201			

On summing this with $u^{(0)}$ and computing the solution at the remaining mesh points by means of

$$u_{i,k} = \tfrac{1}{4}(u_{i,k+1} + u_{i-1,k} + u_{i,k-1} + u_{i+1,k}),$$

we arrive at the values of $u_{i,k}$ shown in Fig. 5. This result is slightly more accurate than the one given in D. Yu. Panov's handbook on the numerical solution of differential equations, which was obtained after 40 iterations.

		0	0	0	0	0	
15.45		11.71	8.87	6.48	4.28	2.14	0
29.39		22.52	17.28	12.79	8.54	4.28	0
40.45		31.70	24.94	18.86	12.79	6.48	0
47.56		38.91	31.92	24.94	17.28	8.87	0
50.00		44.46	38.91	31.70	22.52	11.71	0

50.00 47.56 40.45 29.39 15.45

FIG. 5.

CHAPTER V

Solution of Time-Dependent Problems by the Method of Moments

I. Equations with Positive Definite Operators

The fact that a linear operator can be approximated by the method of moments permits a considerable broadening of the range of applicability of iterative methods. In particular, we are going to show that the method of moments may be applied with great success in solving diverse time-dependent problems. We begin with the solution of the Cauchy problem for a partial differential equation of first order (with respect to t)

$$\frac{\partial x}{\partial t} = -Ax, \tag{1}$$

with x an element of the Hilbert space H and A a positive definite symmetric linear operator defined on an everywhere dense set of H.

In general, A is an unbounded operator. The initial data for (1) at $t = 0$ is

$$x(0) = x_0 \in H.$$

Since A is positive definite, it possesses a bounded inverse, which we shall assume to be defined over all of H.

We can then write (1) in the form

$$A^{-1}\frac{\partial x}{\partial t} + x = 0. \tag{1'}$$

Setting $z_0 = x_0, z_1 = A^{-1}z_0, \ldots, z_n = A^{-1}z_{n-1}, \ldots$, we construct the

sequence A_n of solutions of problems of moments, and we replace (1')
by the equation

$$A_n \frac{\partial x_n}{\partial t} + x_n = 0 \tag{2}$$

close to it with the initial condition $x_n(0) = x_0$.

If we introduce the spectral function $\mathscr{E}_\lambda$ of the inverse operator A^{-1},
the required solution can be expressed as

$$x = \int_0^M e^{-t/\lambda} d\mathscr{E}_\lambda x_0,$$

with M the least upper bound of the spectrum of A^{-1} and so equal
to $\|A^{-1}\|$.

Since $e^{-t/\lambda}$ is continuous for $\lambda \geq 0$ for all $t \geq 0$ and since the strong
convergence of a sequence of operators implies the strong convergence
of a continuous function of them, it follows that the sequence x_n of
solutions of (2) converges (strongly) to x, i.e.,

$$\|x_n - x\| \xrightarrow[n \to \infty]{} 0.$$

The convergence is of course not uniform with respect to time.

Let us next show how the approximate solution x_n may be computed.
Set

$$x_n = \eta_0(t)z_0 + \eta_1(t)z_1 + \ldots + \eta_{n-1}(t)z_{n-1},$$

and substitute this in equation (2). Using the formulas (8) of Chapter I,
we obtain

$$\eta_0 z_0 + \left(\eta_1 + \frac{d\eta_0}{dt}\right)z_1 + \ldots + \left(\eta_{n-1} + \frac{d\eta_{n-2}}{dt}\right)z_{n-1} + \frac{d\eta_{n-1}}{dt} E_n z_n = 0.$$

The application of the expression

$$E_n z_n = -\alpha_0 z_0 - \alpha_1 z_1 - \ldots - \alpha_{n-1} z_{n-1}$$

[see formula (9) of Chapter I] yields

$$\left(\eta_0 - \alpha_0 \frac{d\eta_{n-1}}{dt}\right)z_0 + \left(\eta_1 + \frac{d\eta_0}{dt} - \alpha_1 \frac{d\eta_{n-1}}{dt}\right)z_1 + \ldots$$

$$\ldots + \left(\eta_{n-1} + \frac{d\eta_{n-2}}{dt} - \alpha_{n-1} \frac{d\eta_{n-1}}{dt}\right)z_{n-1} = 0.$$

Since $z_0, z_1, \ldots, z_{n-1}$ are by assumption linearly independent (otherwise, as repeatedly mentioned, the approximation procedure would break off earlier and the exact solution would be obtained), by equating their coefficients to zero, we arrive at a system of scalar equations equivalent to (2):

$$\left.\begin{array}{c} \eta_0 - \alpha_0 \dfrac{d\eta_{n-1}}{dt} = 0, \\[2mm] \dfrac{d\eta_0}{dt} + \eta_1 - \alpha_1 \dfrac{d\eta_{n-1}}{dt} = 0, \\[2mm] \cdot \quad \cdot \quad \cdot \quad \cdot \quad \cdot \quad \cdot \quad \cdot \quad \cdot \quad \cdot \quad \cdot \\[2mm] \dfrac{d\eta_{n-2}}{dt} + \eta_{n-1} - \alpha_{n-1} \dfrac{d\eta_{n-1}}{dt} = 0 \end{array}\right\} \qquad (3)$$

with corresponding initial conditions

$$\eta_0(0) = 1, \quad \eta_1(0) = \eta_2(0) = \ldots = \eta_{n-1}(0) = 0.$$

Equations (3) may be solved by means of Laplace transforms. Let

$$\xi_k = \int_0^\infty \eta_k e^{-\lambda t} dt.$$

Then

$$\left.\begin{array}{c} \xi_0 - \alpha_0 \lambda \xi_{n-1} = 0, \\[2mm] \lambda \xi_0 + \xi_1 - \alpha_1 \lambda \xi_{n-1} = 1, \\[2mm] \cdot \quad \cdot \quad \cdot \quad \cdot \quad \cdot \quad \cdot \quad \cdot \quad \cdot \quad \cdot \quad \cdot \quad \cdot \\[2mm] \lambda \xi_{n-2} + \xi_{n-1} - \alpha_{n-1} \lambda \xi_{n-1} = 0, \end{array}\right\}$$

and hence

$$\xi_j = \frac{P_{n-j-1}\left(-\dfrac{1}{\lambda}\right)}{\lambda^2 P_n\left(-\dfrac{1}{\lambda}\right)} \quad (j \geqq 1),$$

$$\xi_0 = \frac{\alpha_0}{\lambda P_n\left(-\dfrac{1}{\lambda}\right)}.$$

Here, $P_n(v) = v^n + \alpha_{n-1} v^{n-1} + \ldots + \alpha_0$ is the n-th orthogonal polynomial, the roots of which are all real and lie in the interval $[0, M]$.

The solution of (3) is thus given by the contour integrals

$$\eta_j(t) = \frac{1}{2\pi i} \int_{\sigma-i\infty}^{\sigma+i\infty} \frac{P_{n-j-1}\left(-\dfrac{1}{\lambda}\right)}{\lambda^2 P_n\left(-\dfrac{1}{\lambda}\right)} e^{\lambda t} \, d\lambda \quad (j \geq 1),$$

$$\eta_0(t) = \frac{1}{2\pi i} \int_{\sigma-i\infty}^{\sigma+i\infty} \frac{\alpha_0 \, e^{\lambda t}}{\lambda P_n\left(-\dfrac{1}{\lambda}\right)} \, d\lambda,$$

which may be evaluated by means of residues.

The non-homogeneous problem

$$\frac{\partial x}{\partial t} = -Ax + gf(t), \tag{4}$$

$x(0) = 0$, with $g \in H$ and $f(t)$ a scalar function, may be solved in a similar way.

The desired solution is

$$x = \int_0^M \left[\int_0^t f(\xi) e^{-(t-\xi)/\lambda} \, d\xi \right] d\mathscr{E}_\lambda g$$

and is a continuous function of the inverse operator. Therefore, the sequence x_n of solutions of

$$A_n \frac{\partial x_n}{\partial t} + x_n = A^{-1} gf(t), \tag{5}$$

with A_n the operator furnishing a solution to the problem of moments defined by $z_0 = g,\ z_1 = A^{-1}g, \ldots, z_n = A^{-1}z_{n-1}, \ldots$, converges (strongly) to x when n approaches infinity.

We again look for an approximate solution x_n of the form

$$x_n = \eta_0(t)z_0 + \eta_1(t)z_1 + \ldots + \eta_{n-1}(t)z_{n-1}.$$

The substitution of this in equation (5) leads to a system of scalar equations

$$
\left.
\begin{array}{c}
\eta_0 - \alpha_0 \dfrac{d\eta_{n-1}}{dt} = 0, \\[2ex]
\dfrac{d\eta_0}{dt} + \eta_1 - \alpha_1 \dfrac{d\eta_{n-1}}{dt} = f(t), \\[1ex]
\cdot \;\; \cdot \;\; \cdot \;\; \cdot \;\; \cdot \;\; \cdot \;\; \cdot \;\; \cdot \;\; \cdot \;\; \cdot \;\; \cdot \\[1ex]
\dfrac{d\eta_{n-2}}{dt} + \eta_{n-1} - \alpha_{n-1} \dfrac{d\eta_{n-1}}{dt} = 0,
\end{array}
\right\}
$$

which can be solved by Laplace transforms to obtain

$$
\eta_j = \frac{1}{2\pi i} \int_{\sigma - i\infty}^{\sigma + i\infty} \frac{F(\lambda) P_{n-j-1}\left(-\dfrac{1}{\lambda}\right)}{\lambda^2 P_n\left(-\dfrac{1}{\lambda}\right)} \, e^{\lambda t} d\lambda \quad (j \geqq 1),
$$

$$
\eta_0 = \frac{1}{2\pi i} \int_{\sigma - i\infty}^{\sigma + i\infty} \frac{\alpha_0 \, e^{\lambda t} F(\lambda)}{\lambda P_n\left(-\dfrac{1}{\lambda}\right)} \, d\lambda,
$$

where
$$
F(\lambda) = \int_0^\infty f(t) e^{-\lambda t} d\lambda.
$$

We next consider some oscillation problems characterized by a partial differential equation of second order with respect to time

$$
\frac{\partial^2 x}{\partial t^2} = -Ax, \tag{6}
$$

with A a positive definite symmetric operator as before and with initial data prescribed at $t = 0$:

$$
x(0) = x_0, \quad \frac{\partial x(0)}{\partial t} = \dot{x}_0.
$$

By use of the spectral function of the inverse operator, the solution of equation (6) can be written in the form

$$
x = \int_0^M \cos \sqrt{\left(\frac{1}{\lambda}\right)} t \, d\mathscr{E}_\lambda x_0 + \int_0^M \sqrt{(\lambda)} \sin \sqrt{\left(\frac{1}{\lambda}\right)} t \, d\mathscr{E}_\lambda \dot{x}_0. \tag{7}
$$

Here, M is the least upper bound of the spectrum of A^{-1}, which means $M = \|A^{-1}\|$. Generally speaking, the expression (7) is a generalized solution since x_0 and $\dot{x}_0$ may not belong to the domain of the operator A.

The solution (7) has been represented as a sum of two particular solutions. Let us show how each can be determined by the method of moments. For definiteness, consider the first solution

$$x^{(1)} = \int_0^M \cos\sqrt{\left(\frac{1}{\lambda}\right)} t \, d\mathscr{E}_\lambda x_0.$$

Setting $z_0 = x_0, z_1 = A^{-1}z_0, \ldots, z_n = A^{-1}z_{n-1}, \ldots$ and solving the corresponding problem of moments, we find the operator A_n. We then replace equation (6) by the approximation

$$A_n \frac{\partial^2 x_n^{(1)}}{\partial t^2} = x_n^{(1)}, \qquad (8)$$

whose solution is given by

$$x_n^{(1)} = \int_0^M \cos\sqrt{\left(\frac{1}{\lambda}\right)} t \, d\mathscr{E}_\lambda^{(n)} x_0.$$

We now show that as n approaches infinity, the sequence $x_n^{(1)}$ converges (strongly) to the desired solution $x^{(1)}$.

Since the operator A inverse to A^{-1} exists, zero is not an eigenvalue of A^{-1}. Hence, its spectral function $\mathscr{E}_\lambda$ is continuous at zero. Therefore, given any $\varepsilon > 0$, there exists a $\delta > 0$ such that

$$\left\| \int_0^\delta \cos\sqrt{\left(\frac{1}{\lambda}\right)} t \, d\mathscr{E}_\lambda x_0 \right\| \leq \| \mathscr{E}_\delta x_0 \| < \frac{\varepsilon}{8}.$$

If δ is not in the discrete spectrum of A^{-1}, which may always be assumed to hold because the eigenvalues comprise a denumerable set, it follows that $\mathscr{E}_\delta^{(n)} x_0 \Rightarrow \mathscr{E}_\delta x_0$. Thus, for n sufficiently large,

$$\| \mathscr{E}_\delta^{(n)} x_0 - \mathscr{E}_\delta x_0 \| < \frac{\varepsilon}{8}.$$

Hence,

$$\left\| \int_0^\delta \cos\sqrt{\left(\frac{1}{\lambda}\right)} t \, d\mathscr{E}_\lambda^{(n)} x_0 \right\| \leq \| \mathscr{E}_\delta^{(n)} x_0 \|$$

$$\leq \| \mathscr{E}_\delta^{(n)} x_0 - \mathscr{E}_\delta x_0 \| + \| \mathscr{E}_\delta x_0 \| \leq \frac{\varepsilon}{4}.$$

We then have

$$\|x^{(1)} - x_n^{(1)}\| \leq \left\| \int_0^M \cos\sqrt{\left(\frac{1}{\lambda}\right)}t\, d\mathcal{E}_\lambda x_0 - \int_0^M \cos\sqrt{\left(\frac{1}{\lambda}\right)}t\, d\mathcal{E}_{(\lambda)}^{(n)} x_0 \right\|$$

$$\leq \left\| \int_\delta^M \cos\sqrt{\left(\frac{1}{\lambda}\right)}t\, d\mathcal{E}_\lambda x_0 - \int_\delta^M \cos\sqrt{\left(\frac{1}{\lambda}\right)}t\, d\mathcal{E}_\lambda^{(n)} x_0 \right\|$$

$$+ \left\| \int_0^\delta \cos\sqrt{\left(\frac{1}{\lambda}\right)}t\, d\mathcal{E}_\lambda x_0 \right\| + \left\| \int_0^\delta \cos\sqrt{\left(\frac{1}{\lambda}\right)}t\, d\mathcal{E}_\lambda^{(n)} x_0 \right\|.$$

Now $\cos t\sqrt{(1/\lambda)}$ is a continuous function of λ in the interval $[\delta, M]$ $(M > 0)$, and so for n sufficiently large

$$\left\| \int_\delta^M \cos\sqrt{\left(\frac{1}{\lambda}\right)}t\, d\mathcal{E}_\lambda x_0 - \int_\delta^M \cos\sqrt{\left(\frac{1}{\lambda}\right)}t\, d\mathcal{E}_\lambda^{(n)} x_0 \right\| < \frac{\varepsilon}{2}.$$

Combining the above inequalities, we obtain

$$\|x^{(1)} - x_n^{(1)}\| < \varepsilon,$$

q.e.d.

The proof is slightly simpler for the second solution in (7) due to $\sqrt{\lambda} \sin t\sqrt{(1/\lambda)}$ being continuous for $\lambda \geq 0$.

We next indicate how the approximate solutions $x_n^{(1)}$ and $x_n^{(2)}$ can be computed.

As usual, we look for a solution of (8) of the form

$$x_n^{(1)} = \eta_0 z_0 + \eta_1 z_1 + \ldots + \eta_{n-1} z_{n-1}.$$

The substitution of this in (8) leads to a system of scalar equations

$$\left.\begin{array}{c} \eta_0 - \alpha_0 \dfrac{d^2\eta_{n-1}}{dt^2} = 0, \\[2ex] \dfrac{d^2\eta_0}{dt^2} + \eta_1 - \alpha_1 \dfrac{d^2\eta_{n-1}}{dt^2} = 0, \\[2ex] \cdots \cdots \cdots \cdots \cdots \\[2ex] \dfrac{d^2\eta_{n-2}}{dt^2} + \eta_{n-1} - \alpha_{n-1} \dfrac{d^2\eta_{n-1}}{dt^2} = 0 \end{array}\right\} \qquad (9)$$

with the initial conditions

$$\eta_0 = 1, \quad \eta_1 = \eta_2 = \ldots = \eta_{n-1} = 0,$$

$$(t = 0)$$

$$\frac{d\eta_0}{dt} = \frac{d\eta_1}{dt} = \ldots = \frac{d\eta_{n-1}}{dt} = 0.$$

The integration of these equations is perfectly analogous to that of the system (3).

The second solution is also calculated in exactly the same way. Setting $z_0 = \dot{x}_0, z_1 = A^{-1}z_0, \ldots, z_n = A^{-1}z_{n-1}, \ldots$, we obtain a system of the form (9) but with different coefficients α_i and with initial conditions

$$\eta_0 = \ldots = \eta_{n-1} = 0,$$

$$\frac{d\eta_0}{dt} = 1, \quad \frac{d\eta_1}{dt} = \ldots = \frac{d\eta_{n-1}}{dt} = 0.$$

Consider now the non-homogeneous equation

$$\frac{\partial^2 x}{\partial t^2} = -Ax + gf(t), \tag{10}$$

with $g \in H$ and $f(t)$ a scalar function. The initial conditions are assumed to be homogeneous. The solution of (10) can be expressed in integral form by use of the spectral function of the inverse operator as follows:

$$x = \int_0^M \sqrt{(\lambda)} \int_0^t f(\xi) \sin \frac{t - \xi}{\sqrt{(\lambda)}} d\xi \, d\mathscr{E}_\lambda g.$$

It is a continuous function of the operator A^{-1}. Therefore, if we set $z_0 = g, z_1 = A^{-1}z_0, \ldots, z_n = A^{-1}z_{n-1}, \ldots$ and solve the associated problem of moments, the sequence x_n of solutions of

$$A_n \frac{\partial^2 x_n}{\partial t^2} + x_n = A^{-1}gf(t) \tag{11}$$

will converge (strongly) to the solution x. The x_n are determined as usual.

Let

$$x_n = \eta_0(t)z_0 + \eta_1(t)z_1 + \ldots + \eta_{n-1}(t)z_{n-1}$$

and insert this in equation (11). This yields

$$\eta_0 - \alpha_0 \frac{d^2 \eta_{n-1}}{dt^2} = 0,$$

$$\frac{d^2 \eta_0}{dt^2} + \eta_1 - \alpha_1 \frac{d^2 \eta_{n-1}}{dt^2} = f(t),$$

$$\cdot \quad \cdot \quad \cdot \quad \cdot \quad \cdot \quad \cdot \quad \cdot \quad \cdot \quad \cdot \quad \cdot$$

$$\frac{d^2 \eta_{n-2}}{dt^2} + \eta_{n-1} - \alpha_{n-1} \frac{d^2 \eta_{n-1}}{dt^2} = 0.$$

Laplace transforms can again be used to solve these equations, the result being

$$\eta_j = \frac{1}{2\pi i} \int_{\sigma - i\infty}^{\sigma + i\infty} \frac{F(\lambda) P_{n-j-1}\left(-\dfrac{1}{\lambda^2}\right)}{\lambda^4 P_n\left(-\dfrac{1}{\lambda^2}\right)} e^{\lambda t}\, d\lambda \quad (j \geqq 1),$$

$$\eta_0 = \frac{1}{2\pi i} \int_{\sigma - i\infty}^{\sigma + i\infty} \frac{\alpha_0 F(\lambda) e^{\lambda t}}{\lambda^2 P_n\left(-\dfrac{1}{\lambda^2}\right)}\, d\lambda.$$

The integrals can be evaluated by means of residues.

It might be noted that to compute the approximate solution x_n, it is sometimes more convenient to represent it in the form

$$x_n = \eta_0(t) g_0 + \eta_1(t) g_1 + \ldots + \eta_{n-1}(t) g_{n-1},$$

with $g_0, \ldots, g_{n-1}$ appropriately chosen elements of H_n. For example, the g_k could be the elements p_k obtained by orthogonalization of the sequence z_k. The equations for determining the coefficients $\eta_k(t)$ are easily obtained from the corresponding equations (2), (5), (8), and (11).

When investigating the oscillations of conservative systems, one often has to deal with equations of a more general form than the equations (6) and (10) we have considered.

Let the deviation of a system from equilibrium be described by an element x of the Hilbert space H. Under assumptions set down in the theory of small oscillations, the kinetic and potential energies are quadratic forms

$$T = (Mx, x), \quad V = (Ax, x),$$

in which M and A are symmetric operators. Owing to the positive character of the kinetic energy, M is always a positive definite operator. If the equilibrium configuration of an oscillating system is stable in the Lagrangian sense, the operator A is also positive definite.

The equation describing small oscillations has the form

$$M\frac{\partial^2 x}{\partial t^2} + Ax = 0. \tag{12}$$

This equation can be reduced to the equation (6). For, M is positive definite and so (12) can be written as

$$\frac{\partial^2 x}{\partial t^2} + M^{-1}Ax = 0.$$

However, the operator $M^{-1}A$ is non-symmetric. By a change in the definition of the scalar product, $A' = M^{-1}A$ can be turned into a symmetric operator.

To this end, we introduce a new space H' consisting of the elements of H but in which the scalar product is defined as follows:

$$[x, y] = (x, My).$$

The parentheses denote the scalar product in the original space H, while the brackets denote it in the new space H'. The symmetry of A' is then implied by the equalities

$$[A'x, y] = (Ax, y) = (x, Ay) = [x, M^{-1}Ay] = [x, A'y].$$

Thus, the method of moments can be used to solve many time-dependent boundary value problems, in particular, those involving equations with variable coefficients (functions of the coordinates only) where the method of separation of variables often fails to work.

2. Oscillatory Systems with a Finite Number of Degrees of Freedom

The theory of small oscillations has been fairly well worked out for systems with a finite number of degrees of freedom characterized by ordinary differential equations with constant coefficients and has been widely used to solve various physical and engineering problems. It has been especially extensively applied to electric circuits, servomechanisms, and automatic control systems.

The investigation of an oscillating system is usually begun with the consideration of a linear problem if it is a priori unclear as to whether the system should operate under auto-oscillating conditions. At the very beginning, the researcher is already confronted with a number of difficulties. First of all, to carry out a theoretical analysis of a real system, he has to replace it by an idealization, whose motion is studied from that point on. In this connexion, the closer the ideal system reflects the processes going on in the real system, the higher, as a rule, will the order of the system of differential equations describing its motion be. Therefore, the desire to have the best possible description of the motion of a system while remaining within the framework of small oscillations leads to the mathematical problem of studying and solving a system of linear differential equations of high order.

In such problems, the classical methods which have an algebraic basis are no longer adequate and it becomes necessary to resort to approximative techniques.

We shall consider two problems which are closely related to one another. The first one is that of solving a high order system of ordinary linear differential equations with constant coefficients, where algebraic methods no longer prove to be effective. The second is the problem of reducing the order of the system of differential equations. More precisely speaking, the second is that of replacing the given system by an approximate one close to it but of lower order. By close, we mean a system whose solutions stay close to the solutions of the original system under identical perturbations.

At first glance, the second problem appears to be meaningless. An N-th order system has N eigenoscillations each of which may be excited by the application of a suitable choice of external forces to the physical system. In the reduction of the order of the system, not only would the eigenoscillations be distorted but they would also be reduced in number, and thus some of them would cease to play a part. Therefore, the overall oscillations of the "close" system could be expected to differ markedly from those of the original if the external forces acting on the system have been so chosen as to excite the missing eigenoscillations. However, for real systems, the external forces are far from being arbitrary. Usually one or several members of a physical system are subjected to perturbations, the other being unaffected and displaced only as a result of their relationship to the other members. Under these conditions, certain eigenoscillations may, generally speaking, either not be excited or be excited so little as to have no appreciable effect on the overall oscillations. Under these circumstances, the problem of reducing the order of a system of differential equations is now a meaningful and a very urgent one since the order of a system is often determined not by the physical essence of the problem but by the degree of idealization that we have adopted.

Let the deviation of a system from equilibrium be defined by a vector x in N-dimensional space H. We shall suppose that the system of equations describing the motion of the physical system has been reduced to the normal form

$$\frac{dx}{dt} = Ax + g\, f(t). \tag{13}$$

Here, A is a linear operator (matrix) in H, $g f(t)$ is the driving force, the vector g being its "amplitude", and $f(t)$ is a scalar function. The initial conditions are assumed to be zero. Later on, we shall also treat the Cauchy problem.

To solve (13), we again apply the method of moments. Set $z_0 = g$ and form the iterations

$$z_0 = g, \quad z_1 = Az_0, \ldots, z_n = A^n z_0 = Az_{n-1}, \ldots$$

We tentatively suppose that the z_k are linearly independent.

The solution of the problem of moments is an operator A_n defined on the subspace H_n generated by all linear combinations of $z_0, z_1, \ldots, z_{n-1}$ such that

$$\left. \begin{array}{l} z_k = A_n^k z_0 \quad (k = 0, 1, \ldots, n-1), \\[2mm] E_n z_n = A_n^n z_0, \end{array} \right\} \tag{14}$$

with E_n the operator projecting onto H_n. Since $E_n z_n$ belongs to H_n, there exist numbers $\alpha_1, \ldots, \alpha_n$ such that

$$E_n z_n = A_n^n z_0 = -\alpha_0 z_0 - \alpha_1 z_1 - \ldots - \alpha_{n-1} z_{n-1}, \tag{15}$$

or

$$P_n^*(A_n)z_0 = (A_n^n + \alpha_{n-1} A_n^{n-1} + \ldots + \alpha_1 A_n + \alpha_0 I)z_0 = 0. \tag{16}$$

Hence, the roots of $P_n(\lambda)$ are the eigenvalues of A_n. Taking the scalar product of (15) with $z_0, \ldots, z_{n-1}$, respectively, we obtain a system of linear algebraic equations for the coefficients α_k, namely,

$$
\left.
\begin{aligned}
(z_0, z_0)\alpha_0 + (z_0, z_1)\alpha_1 + \ldots + (z_0, z_{n-1})\alpha_{n-1} + (z_0, z_n) &= 0, \\
(z_1, z_0)\alpha_0 + (z_1, z_1)\alpha_1 + \ldots + (z_1, z_{n-1})\alpha_{n-1} + (z_1, z_n) &= 0, \\
\cdot \ \\
(z_{n-1}, z_0)\alpha_0 + (z_{n-1}, z_1)\alpha_1 + \ldots + (z_{n-1}, z_{n-1})\alpha_{n-1} + (z_{n-1}, z_n) &= 0.
\end{aligned}
\right\}
$$

$$(17)$$

As shown earlier, $A_n \to A$ when n tends to infinity, and therefore an approximate solution to (13) can be found by solving

$$\frac{dx_n}{dt} = A_n x_n + g\, f(t). \tag{18}$$

Now x_n belongs to H_n and can be represented as

$$x_n = \eta_0(t)z_0 + \eta_1(t)z_1 + \ldots + \eta_{n-1}(t)z_{n-1}, \tag{19}$$

with $\eta_0(t), \eta_1(t), \ldots, \eta_{n-1}(t)$ scalar functions. The substitution of (19) into (18) and the application of formula (15) then leads to

$$
\left(\frac{d\eta_0}{dt} + \alpha_0\eta_{n-1}\right)z_0 + \left(\frac{d\eta_1}{dt} - \eta_0 + \alpha_1\eta_{n-1}\right)z_1 + \ldots
$$
$$
\ldots + \left(\frac{d\eta_{n-1}}{dt} - \eta_{n-2} + \alpha_{n-1}\eta_{n-1}\right)z_{n-1} = z_0 \cdot f(t).
$$

Equating like coefficients, we arrive at the following system of scalar equations equivalent to the vector equation (18):

$$
\left.
\begin{aligned}
\frac{d\eta_0}{dt} + \alpha_0\eta_{n-1} &= f(t), \\
\frac{d\eta_1}{dt} - \eta_0 + \alpha_1\eta_{n-1} &= 0, \\
\cdot \ \cdot \ \cdot \ \cdot \ \cdot \ \cdot \ \cdot \ \cdot \ \cdot \ \cdot \ \\
\frac{d\eta_{n-1}}{dt} - \eta_{n-2} + \alpha_{n-1}\eta_{n-1} &= 0
\end{aligned}
\right\}
$$

$$(20)$$

with initial conditions $\eta_0(0) = \eta_1(0) = \ldots = \eta_{n-1}(0) = 0$.

These equations may be solved, for example, as follows. The roots of the characteristic equation

$$P_n(\lambda) = \lambda^n + \alpha_{n-1}\lambda^{n-1} + \ldots + \alpha_0 = 0$$

are first determined. Then from the equation

$$\eta_{n-1}^{(n)} + \alpha_{n-1}\eta_{n-1}^{(n-1)} + \ldots + \alpha_0 \eta_{n-1} = f(t) \tag{21}$$

$\eta_{n-1}(t)$ is found subject to the initial conditions $\eta_{n-1}(0) = \eta'_{n-1}(0) = \ldots = \eta_{n-1}^{(n-1)}(0) = 0$. Afterwards, the remaining unknowns are determined from the system (20) by means of quadrature.

We next consider to what extent $x_n(t)$ may be regarded as an approximate solution of the original system of differential equations (13).

If the vectors $z_0, z_1, \ldots, z_n$ are not linearly independent, and say, z_n is linearly dependent on $z_0, \ldots, z_{n-1}$, then $E_n z_n = z_n$ and as was indicated above, the operators A and A_n coincide. In that event, the approximate solution coincides with the exact one. This will always hold for $n \geq N$ since the number of linearly independent vectors cannot exceed N, the dimension of the space.

If n is not too large so that $E_n z_n$ is still unequal to z_n, then x_n will not coincide with the exact solution. Let y_n denote the error in the approximate solution, that is,

$$x = x_n + y_n.$$

Substitution of this in (13) yields

$$\frac{d\eta_0}{dt}z_0 + \frac{d\eta_0}{dt}z_1 + \ldots + \frac{d\eta_{n-1}}{dt}z_{n-1} + \frac{dy_n}{dt}$$

$$= \eta_0 z_1 + \eta_1 z_2 + \ldots + \eta_{n-1}E_n z_n + \eta_{n-1}(z_n - E_n z_n) + Ay_n + gf(t),$$

which implies the following equation for the error:

$$\frac{dy_n}{dt} = Ay_n + \eta_{n-1}(t)(z_n - E_n z_n).$$

Moreover, since

$$\eta_{n-1}(0) = \eta'_{n-1}(0) = \ldots = \eta_{n-1}^{(n-1)}(0) = 0,$$

we have

$$y_n(0) = \frac{dy_n(0)}{dt} = \ldots = \frac{d^n y_n(0)}{dt^n} = 0.$$

The error equation and initial conditions show that the error is proportional to $\|z_n - E_n z_n\|$, and if the latter is small the error will also be small. Furthermore, $x_n(t)$ is close to $x(t)$ for small values of t, but in general as time increases, the error in the approximate solution will increase.

Let us indicate two of the more important cases in which the quantity $\| z_n - E_n z_n \|$ is small for $n < N$ and the system of differential equations (13) can be approximated by the lower order system (18).

For simplicity, suppose that the operator A has a simple structure. Then the vector g, the "amplitude" of the external force, can be expanded in terms of its eigenvectors

$$g = \sum_{k=1}^{N} a_k u_k.$$

If the external force is such that some of the eigenoscillations are excited very little, in other words, some of the a_k are small or vanish and

$$\sum_{k=n+1}^{N} |a_k| < \delta,$$

then it is easy to show that $\| z_n - E_n z_n \|$ is small.

For,

$$z_0 = g = \sum_{k=1}^{N} a_k u_k, \quad z_1 = \sum_{k=1}^{N} a_k \lambda_k u_k, \ldots, z_n = \sum_{k=1}^{N} a_k \lambda_k^n u_k.$$

Consider the difference

$$z_n - \overline{z_n} = Q_n(A) z_0,$$

where

$$Q_n(\lambda) = (\lambda - \lambda_1) \ldots (\lambda - \lambda_n).$$

The fact that E_n is a projection implies that

$$\| z_n - E_n z_n \| \leq \| z_n - \overline{z_n} \| = \Big\| \sum_{k=n+1}^{N} Q_n(\lambda_k) a_k u_k \Big\|.$$

Let M denote $\max |Q_n(\lambda_k)|$ and suppose the eigenelements have been normalized. Then $\| z_n - E_n z_n \|$ satisfies the following inequality:

$$\| z_n - E_n z_n \| \leq \delta M.$$

Let us now discuss the second case. Assuming that some of the eigenvalues are small in modulus, namely,

$$|\lambda_k| < \delta \quad (k = m+1, \ldots, N),$$

we form the difference
$$z_n - \tilde{z}_n = G_n(A)z_0,$$
in which
$$G_n(\lambda) = (\lambda - \lambda_1)\ldots(\lambda - \lambda_m)\lambda^{n-m}.$$

By the property of the projection,
$$\| z_n - E_n z_n \| \leq \| z_n - \tilde{z}_n \| = \left\| \sum_{m+1}^{N} \lambda_k^{n-m}(\lambda_k - \lambda_1)\ldots(\lambda_k - \lambda_m)a_k u_k \right\|,$$
and hence,
$$\| z_n - E_n z_n \| \leq \delta^{n-m}(|\lambda_1| + \delta)\ldots(|\lambda_m| + \delta) \sum_{m+1}^{N} |a_k|.$$

Thus, $\| z_n - E_n z_n \|$ will be small when $n > m$ provided the external perturbation is such that the sum
$$\sum_{m+1}^{N} |a_k|$$
is not too big.

For many oscillating systems, the opposite picture holds. With increasing number, the eigenvalues grow rapidly in modulus, and the norm of the operator is large although bounded. The approximations converge considerably faster for such systems if instead of forming iterations with the operator A appearing in the wave equation (13), we use its inverse.

Rewrite equation (13) in the form
$$A^{-1}\frac{dx}{dt} = x + A^{-1}gf(t), \qquad (13')$$

and construct a sequence of iterations by setting $z_0 = A^{-1}g, z_1 = A^{-1}z_0,$ $\ldots, z_n = A^{-1}z_{n-1}$. The vectors $z_0, z_1, \ldots, z_n$ can be determined recursively from the relations
$$Az_0 = g, \quad Az_1 = z_0, \ldots, Az_n = z_{n-1}.$$

The solution of the problems of moments furnishes us with some operator A_n.

We next replace equation (13') by
$$A_n\frac{dx_n}{dt} = x_n + A^{-1}gf(t) \qquad (18')$$

which is "close" to it, and we seek a solution to the latter of the form
$$x_n = \eta_0(t)z_0 + \ldots + \eta_{n-1}(t)z_{n-1}.$$

Substitution in the equation and application of (14) and (15) yields

$$-\left(\eta_0 + \alpha_0 \frac{d\eta_{1-1}}{dt}\right)z_0 + \left(\frac{d\eta_0}{dt} - \eta_1 - \alpha_1 \frac{d\eta_{n-1}}{dt}\right)z_1 + \dots$$

$$\dots + \left(\frac{d\eta_{n-2}}{dt} - \eta_{n-1} - \alpha_{n-1}\frac{d\eta_{n-1}}{dt}\right)z_{n-1} = z_0 f(t).$$

Equating coefficients of like terms, we arrive at a system of scalar equations for the $\eta_k(t)$:

$$\left.\begin{aligned}
-\eta_0 - \alpha_0 \frac{d\eta_{n-1}}{dt} &= f(t), \\
\frac{d\eta_0}{dt} - \eta_1 - \alpha_1 \frac{d\eta_{n-1}}{dt} &= 0, \\
\cdots \cdots \cdots \cdots \cdots \\
\frac{d\eta_{n-2}}{dt} - \eta_{n-1} - \alpha_{n-1}\frac{d\eta_{n-1}}{dt} &= 0
\end{aligned}\right\} \qquad (20')$$

with the initial conditions $\eta_0(0) = \eta_1(0) = \dots = \eta_{n-1}(0) = 0$.

It can be shown that the error in the approximate solution for this case is also proportional to $\|z_n - E_n z_n\|$, which is now small for fairly small values of n since the moduli of the eigenvalues of A^{-1} decrease rapidly.

In conclusion, we note that the eigenoscillation problem defined by the equation

$$\frac{dx}{dt} = Ax,$$

and initial condition $x(0) = x_0$ is easily reduced to the non-homogeneous problem by the substitution

$$x = w + x_0.$$

The vector w satisfies the non-homogeneous equation

$$\frac{dw}{dt} = Aw + Ax_0,$$

which is of the form (13), and the initial condition $w(0) = 0$.

There is a close relationship between the method of moments and the method of determining the spectrum of a matrix due to Academician

A. N. Krylov [1], [2]. His starting point was also a system of differential equations with constant coefficients.

The gist of the reasoning used in this method is as follows. An arbitrary vector x is chosen in N-dimensional space and a sequence of iterations of it with the matrix A is then constructed:

$$x, Ax, \ldots, A^k x.$$

Because of the finite dimensionality of the space, there exists an n such that $A^n x$ is a linear combination of the vectors $A^k x$ $(k < n)$. That is,

$$A^n x + \alpha_{n-1} A^{n-1} x + \ldots + \alpha_0 x = 0 \qquad (22)$$

or $$\phi(A)x = 0.$$

This implies an equation for the eigenvalues

$$\lambda^n + \alpha_{n-1} \lambda^{n-1} + \ldots + \alpha_0 = 0.$$

The coefficients α_k can be found from the system of equations obtained by taking components of the vector equation (22) along the coordinate axes. The subspace H_n generated by the vectors $x, Ax, \ldots,$ $A^{n-1}x$ reduces A, and the only n-th degree polynomial with leading coefficient of unity vanishing in H_n is the $P_n(\lambda)$ of (16). The operators A and A_n coincide in H_n, and $\phi_n(\lambda) = P_n(\lambda)$.

Hence, it follows that the only distinction between the method of moments and Krylov's method for the case of a finite symmetric matrix (where, as previously noted, it coincides with Lanczos' "method of minimal iterations") is their computational schemes.

Thus, our above method of solving the equation for small oscillations is actually an extension of Krylov's method in two directions. First, the choice of initial element in determining the spectrum has been made specific. Namely, a reasonable choice has been shown to be either the vector "amplitude" of the external forces, if a problem in forced oscillations is being solved, or else the initial conditions of the Cauchy problem. Such a choice assures us of obtaining the solution. Second, the fact that the method of moments is invariant to the choice of coordinate system permits its use in constructing an approximate solution when the number of degrees of freedom is very great and solving the equations exactly is difficult.

3. Heat Conduction in an Inhomogeneous Rod

Let us consider the conduction of heat in a rod (plate) with a given heat capacity c, density ρ, and coefficient of thermal conductivity k. The temperature distribution in such a rod satisfies the equation

$$\frac{\partial \phi}{\partial t} = a(x)\frac{\partial^2 \phi}{\partial x^2}, \quad a = \frac{k}{c\rho}, \quad -1 \leqq x \leqq 1.$$

We discuss the case where $a(x) = 1/(1+x^2)$, the initial temperature $\phi(x,0) = (1-x^2)/2$, and at the ends of the rod $\phi(-1,t) = \phi(1,t) = 0$. In this instance,

$$A\phi = -\frac{1}{1+x^2}\frac{\partial^2 \phi}{\partial x^2}, \quad \phi(-1,t) = \phi(1,t) = 0$$

and it can be shown that the operator A is positive definite. The sequence of functions $z_0, z_1, z_2, \dots$ is calculated from the formula

$$z_k(x) = A^{-1}z_{k-1}, \quad z_0 = \tfrac{1}{2}(1-x^2),$$

or
$$z_k''(x) = -(1+x^2)z_{k-1}(x), \quad z_k(-1) = z_k(1) = 0.$$

Integrating these equations, we obtain

$$z_0(x) = \tfrac{1}{2}(1-x^2),$$

$$z_1(x) = \tfrac{1}{60}(14 - 15x^2 + x^6)$$

$$\cdot \quad \cdot \quad \cdot \quad \cdot \quad \cdot \quad \cdot \quad \cdot \quad \cdot \quad \cdot \quad \cdot$$

At this point, it is necessary to define a scalar product. It would be possible to introduce L_2 space in which

$$(z_i, z_k) = \int_{-1}^{1} z_i(x)\, z_k(x)\, dx.$$

However, since the initial temperature distribution is twice differentiable and also satisfies the boundary conditions, it is here convenient to use the definition

$$[z_i, z_k] = (A_0 z_i, z_k) = -\int_{-1}^{1} z_i''(x)z_k(x)\, dx.$$

By now applying the formulas of §1, we can write down the equations leading to the first approximation:

$$n = 1: \qquad \phi_1(x,t) = \eta_0(t)z_0(x),$$

$$\eta_0 - \alpha_0 \frac{d\eta_0}{dt} = 0, \quad \eta_0(0) = 1,$$

$$\alpha_0 = -\frac{[z_1, z_0]}{[z_0, z_0]} = -0.4571$$

and those for the second approximation:

$$n = 2: \quad \phi_2(x,t) = \eta_0(t)z_0(x) + \eta_1(t)z_1(x),$$

$$\eta_0 - \alpha_0 \frac{d\eta_1}{dt} = 0,$$

$$\frac{d\eta_0}{dt} + \eta_1 - \alpha_1 \frac{d\eta_1}{dt} = 0,$$

$$\eta_0(0) = 1, \quad \eta_1(0) = 0,$$

$$\alpha_0 = 10^{-2} \cdot 2.1781, \quad \alpha_1 = -0.50674.$$

On solving the resulting differential equations, we deduce the following values for $\phi_1(x,t)$ and $\phi_2(x,t)$:

$n = 1: \quad \phi_1(x,t) = z_0(x)e^{-2.187t};$

$n = 2: \quad \phi_2(x,t) = [2.428z_1(x) - 0.1151z_0(x)]e^{-2.177t}$
$$- [2.428z_1(x) - 1.1151z_0(x)]e^{-2.109}.$$

The table below gives the temperature distribution in the rod for the first and second approximations at $t = 0.2$.

x	ϕ_1	ϕ_2
0	0.3229	0.3292
0.2	0.3099	0.3151
0.4	0.2712	0.2725
0.6	0.2066	0.2025
0.8	0.1162	0.1087
1.0	0	0

4. The Transient in an Automatic Control System

Consider an automatic velocity-control system with five amplification stages.

The equations of motion governing a schematic control diagram with five consecutively engaged servomotors of single-stage amplification (Fig. 6 depicts the simplest variant of such a diagram) are given by

$$
\left.
\begin{aligned}
&\frac{dx_0}{dt} = -x_1 + f(t), \\[2mm]
&\frac{dx_1}{dt} = \frac{1}{T_1}(x_2 - x_1), &\quad &\frac{dx_4}{dt} = \frac{1}{T_4}(x_5 - x_4), \\[2mm]
&\frac{dx_2}{dt} = \frac{1}{T_2}(x_3 - x_2), &\quad &\frac{dx_5}{dt} = \frac{1}{T_5}(x_0 - x_5). \\[2mm]
&\frac{dx_3}{dt} = \frac{1}{T_3}(x_4 - x_3),
\end{aligned}
\right\}
\tag{23}
$$

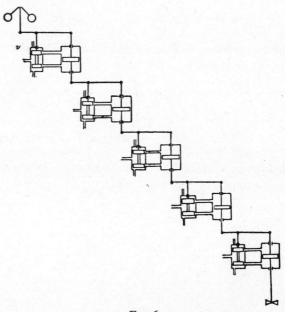

Fig. 6

Here, x_0 is the dimensionless angular velocity of the engine, x_1 through x_5 are the dimensionless coordinates of the pistons in the corresponding servomotors, and $f(t)$ is the external moment applied to the engine shaft.

We are interested in the transient from one stationary state to another. To this end, we must put $f(t) \equiv 1$ and assume $x_0 = x_1 = x_2 = x_3 = x_4 = x_5 = 0$ for $t = 0$.

Consider the six-dimensional vector space with components $x_0, x_1, \ldots, x_5$. The right-hand side of (23) defines a linear transformation (operator) in this space, and hence (23) may be expressed in the form

$$\frac{dx}{dt} = Ax + g. \tag{23'}$$

To solve (23′), we apply the method of moments. We first find a set of basis vectors $z_0, z_1, \ldots$ by iterating the inverse operator in the usual way:

$$Az_0 = g, \quad Az_1 = z_0, \ldots, Az_j = z_{j-1}, \ldots$$

In component form, these equations are equivalent to

$$-x_1^{(j)} = x_0^{(j-1)}, \qquad \frac{1}{T_3}(x_4^{(j)} - x_3^{(j)}) = x_3^{(j-1)},$$

$$\frac{1}{T_1}(x_2^{(j)} - x_1^{(j)}) = x_1^{(j-1)}, \qquad \frac{1}{T_4}(x_5^{(j)} - x_4^{(j)}) = x_4^{(j-1)},$$

$$\frac{1}{T_2}(x_3^{(j)} - x_2^{(j)}) = x_2^{(j-1)}, \qquad \frac{1}{T_5}(x_0^{(j)} - x_5^{(j)}) = x_5^{(j-1)},$$

where $x_0^{(j)}, x_1^{(j)}, \ldots, x_5^{(j)}$ are the components of z_j; the vector z_{-1} is understood to be g. This system implies the following recursion relations for the components of z_j in terms of the components of z_{j-1}:

$$x_1^{(j)} = -x_0^{(j-1)},$$

$$x_2^{(j)} = T_1 x_1^{(j-1)} + x_1^{(j)},$$

$$x_3^{(j)} = T_2 x_2^{(j-1)} + x_2^{(j)},$$

$$x_4^{(j)} = T_3 x_3^{(j-1)} + x_3^{(j)},$$

$$x_5^{(j)} = T_4 x_4^{(j-1)} + x_4^{(j)},$$

$$x_0^{(j)} = T_5 x_5^{(j-1)} + x_5^{(j)}.$$

Given the servomotor times $T_1 = 0.4$, $T_2 = T_3 = 0.2$, and $T_4 = T_5 = 0.1$ and recalling that $z_{-1} = g$ has the components $x_0^{(-1)} = 1, x_1^{(-1)} = x_2^{(-1)} = \ldots = x_5^{(-1)} = 0$, we can find the components of the basis vectors z_k from the recursion relations. The first few results are

$$z_0 = (-1, \ -1, \ -1, \ -1, \ -1, \ -1),$$

$$z_1 = (0, \ 1, \ 0.6, \ 0.4, \ 0.2, \ 0.1),$$

$$z_2 = (0.63, \ 0, \ 0.4, \ 0.52, \ 0.6, \ 0.62),$$

$$z_3 = (-0.324, \ -0.630, \ -0.630, \ -0.550, \ -0.446, \ -0.386),$$

. . . .

The scalar product is the usual sum of products of components, and so
$$(z_0, z_0) = 6, \quad (z_0, z_1) = -2.3,$$

$$(z_1, z_1) = 1.57,$$

$$(z_0, z_2) = -2.77, \quad (z_0, z_3) = 2.966,$$

$$(z_1, z_2) = 0.630, \quad (z_1, z_3) = -1.3558,$$

$$(z_2, z_2) = 1.5777, \quad (z_2, z_3) = -1.24904.$$

The equations for the parameters α_k are therefore

$$n = 1: \qquad 6\alpha_0 - 2.3 = 0;$$

$$n = 2: \quad 6\alpha_0 - 2.3\alpha_1 - 2.77 = 0,$$

$$-2.3\alpha_0 + 1.57\alpha_1 + 0.630 = 0;$$

$$n = 3: \quad 6\alpha_0 - 2.3\alpha_1 - 2.77\alpha_2 + 2.966 = 0,$$

$$-2.3\alpha_0 + 1.57\alpha_1 + 0.630\alpha_2 - 1.3558 = 0,$$

$$-2.77\alpha_0 + 0.630\alpha_1 + 1.5717\alpha_2 - 1.24904 = 0,$$

and hence

$$n = 1: \quad \alpha_0 = 0.3833;$$

$$n = 2: \quad \alpha_0 = 0.7022,$$
$$\alpha_1 = 0.6274;$$

$$n = 3: \quad \alpha_0 = 0.1718,$$
$$\alpha_1 = 0.8042,$$
$$\alpha_2 = 0.7751.$$

The approximate solutions of (23′) are then given by

$$
\left.
\begin{aligned}
n = 1: \quad & x = \eta_0 z_0; \\
n = 2: \quad & x = \eta_0 z_0 + \eta_1 z_1; \\
n = 3: \quad & x = \eta_0 z_0 + \eta_1 z_1 + \eta_2 z_2,
\end{aligned}
\right\}
\tag{24}
$$

in which the functions $\eta_k(t)$ are to be found from the equations

$$
n = 1: \quad -\eta_0 - 0.3833 \frac{d\eta_0}{dt} = 1;
$$

$$
\left.
\begin{aligned}
n = 2: \quad & -\eta_0 - 0.7022 \frac{d\eta_1}{dt} = 1, \\
& \frac{d\eta_0}{dt} - \eta_1 - 0.6274 \frac{d\eta_1}{dt} = 0;
\end{aligned}
\right\}
$$

$$
\left.
\begin{aligned}
n = 3: \quad & -\eta_0 - 0.1718 \frac{d\eta_2}{dt} = 1, \\
& \frac{d\eta_0}{dt} - \eta_1 - 0.8042 \frac{d\eta_2}{dt} = 0, \\
& \frac{d\eta_1}{dt} - \eta_2 - 0.7751 \frac{d\eta_2}{dt} = 0.
\end{aligned}
\right\}
$$

Solving these differential equations under zero initial conditions, we obtain

$n = 1$: $\eta_0 = e^{-2.609t} - 1$;

$n = 2$: $\eta_0 = e^{-0.4469t}(\cos 1.107t - 0.4037 \sin 1.107t) - 1$,

$\eta_1 = -e^{-0.4469t} 1.286 \sin 1.107t$;

$n = 3$: $\eta_0 = 1.111 e^{-3.908t}$

$\qquad - 2e^{-0.3865t}(0.0551 \cos 1.158t - 0.1642 \sin 1.158t) - 1$,

$\eta_1 = 0.8598 e^{-3.908t}$

$\qquad - 2e^{-0.3865t}(0.4299 \cos 1.158t + 0.6420 \sin 1.158t)$,

$\eta_2 = 1.654 e^{-3.908t}$

$\qquad - 2e^{-0.3865t}(0.8274 \cos 1.158t - 0.0038 \sin 1.158t)$.

The insertion of these results in (24) yields the respective approximate solutions. Taking components along the x_0-axis, we then find an expression for the angular velocity of the engine:

$$n = 1: \quad x_0(t) = -\eta_0(t);$$

$$n = 2: \quad x_0(t) = -\eta_0(t);$$

$$n = 3: \quad x_0(t) = -\eta_0(t) + 0.63\eta_2(t).$$

The substitution of the expressions for $\eta_0(t)$, $\eta_1(t)$, and $\eta_2(t)$ finally yields

$$n = 1: \quad x_0(t) = 1 - e^{-2.609t};$$

$$n = 2: \quad x_0(t) = 1 - e^{-0.4469t}(\cos 1.107t - 0.4037 \sin 1.107t);$$

$$n = 3: \quad x_0(t) = 1 - 0.069e^{-3.908t}$$
$$- e^{-0.3865t}(0.932 \cos 1.158t - 0.3236 \sin 1.158t).$$

Fig. 7 compares the graphs of the three approximations corresponding to $n = 1, 2, 3$ and the exact solution calculated by numerical integra-

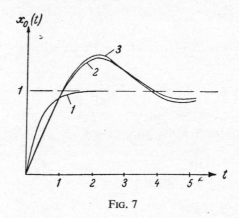

FIG. 7

tion. The third approximation coincides with the exact solution to three decimal places and so their graphs have coalesced. For practical purposes, the second approximation already suffices.

5. Oscillations of an Aeroplane with a Sperry Automatic Pilot

Let us consider the transient in a system consisting of an aeroplane with automatic pilot characterized by the sixth order linear differential equation

$$\frac{d^6 x}{dt^6} + 16.4\frac{d^5 x}{dt^5} + 107.4\frac{d^4 x}{dt^4} + 364.2\frac{d^3 x}{dt^3}$$
$$+1146.2\frac{d^2 x}{dt^2} + 771.2\frac{dx}{dt} + 292.1x = 0. \quad (25)$$

The unknown function $x(t)$ has to satisfy the following initial conditions at $t = 0$:

$$x(0) = 0, \quad x'(0) = 20, \quad x''(0) = x'''(0) = x^{IV}(0) = x^{V}(0) = 0.$$

(See G. Sh. Ioffe [1] and V. V. Solodovnikov [1]). We convert the differential equation (25) into a system by letting

$$x_0 = x, \qquad x_2 = x'', \quad x_4 = x^{IV},$$
$$x_1 = x' - 20, \quad x_3 = x''', \quad x_5 = x^{V}.$$

There results

$$x_0' = x_1 + 20,$$
$$x_1' = x_2,$$
$$x_2' = x_3,$$
$$x_3' = x_4, \qquad\qquad\qquad\qquad (25')$$
$$x_4' = x_5,$$
$$x_5' = -16.4x_5 - 107.4x_4 - 364.2x_3 - 1146.2x_2 - 771.2x_1$$
$$- 292.1x_0 - 1542.4.$$

At $t = 0$, $x_0 = x_1 = x_2 = x_3 = x_4 = x_5 = 0$.

As in the previous application, we introduce six-dimensional vector space with components $x_0, x_1, \ldots, x_5$. The right-hand side of (25') defines a linear operator in this space, and the system (25') may be written in the form

$$\frac{dy}{dt} = Ay + g, \qquad\qquad (25'')$$

where g has the components

$$g_0 = 20, \quad g_1 = 0, \quad g_2 = 0, \quad g_3 = 0, \quad g_4 = 0, \quad g_5 = -1542.4,$$

and $y(0) = 0$. We then find the set of basis vectors $z_0, z_1, \ldots$ by iterating the inverse operator, namely,

$$Az_0 = g, \quad Az_1 = z_0, \ldots, Az_j = z_{j-1}, \ldots$$

In component form, these vector equations are equivalent to

$$x_1^{(j)} = x_0^{(j-1)}, \quad x_2^{(j)} = x_1^{(j-1)}, \quad x_3^{(j)} = x_2^{(j-1)},$$

$$x_4^{(j)} = x_3^{(j-1)}, \quad x_5^{(j)} = x_4^{(j-1)},$$

$$-16.4x_5^{(j)} - 107.4x_4^{(j)} - 364.2x_3^{(j)} - 1146.2x_2^{(j)}$$

$$-771.2x_1^{(j)} - 292.1x_0^{(j)} = x_5^{(j-1)},$$

with $x_0^{(j)}, x_1^{(j)}, \ldots, x_5^{(j)}$ the components of z_j. From this, we then obtain recursion formulas for the components of z_j in terms of the components of z_{j-1}:

$$x_0^{(j)} = -2.64020x_0^{(j-1)} - 3.92400x_1^{(j-1)} - 1.24684x_2^{(j-1)}$$

$$-0.36768x_3^{(j-1)} - 0.056145x_4^{(j-1)} - 0.0034235x_5^{(j-1)},$$

$$x_1^{(j)} = x_0^{(j-1)}, \quad x_2^{(j)} = x_1^{(j-1)}, \quad x_3^{(j)} = x_2^{(j-1)},$$

$$x_4^{(j)} = x_3^{(j-1)}, \quad x_5^{(j)} = x_4^{(j-1)}.$$

Letting $z_{-1} = g$, we compute the three vectors z_0, z_1, and z_2 from these recursion formulas. There results

$$z_0 = (0, \quad 20, \quad 0, \quad 0, \quad 0, \quad 0),$$

$$z_1 = (-78.4800, \quad 0, \quad 20, \quad 0, \quad 0, \quad 0).$$

$$z_2 = (182.266, \quad -78.4800, \quad 0, \quad 20, \quad 0, \quad 0).$$

The scalar product we again define as the sum of products of components and obtain

$$(z_0, z_0) = 400, \quad (z_0, z_1) = 0, \quad (z_0, z_2) = -1569.6,$$

$$(z_1, z_1) = 6559.1, \quad (z_1, z_2) = 14304.2,$$

The equations and values of the parameters α_k are

$$n = 1: \quad \alpha_0 = 0;$$

$$n = 2: \quad 400\alpha_0 - 1569.6 = 0, \qquad \alpha_0 = 3.9240,$$

$$6559.1\alpha_1 - 14304.2 = 0, \quad \alpha_1 = 2.1808.$$

The respective approximate solutions of (25′) are in turn given by

$$\left. \begin{array}{l} n = 1: \quad y = \eta_0 z_0; \\[2mm] n = 2: \quad y = \eta_0 z_0 + \eta_1 z_1, \end{array} \right\} \tag{26}$$

in which the functions $\eta_k(t)$ are determined by the equations

$$n = 1: \qquad -\eta_0 = 1;$$

$$\left. \begin{array}{l} n = 2: \qquad -\eta_0 - 3.9240\dfrac{d\eta_1}{dt} = 1, \\[4mm] \dfrac{d\eta_0}{dt} - \eta_1 - 2.1808\dfrac{d\eta_1}{dt} = 0. \end{array} \right\}$$

Solving these equations under zero initial conditions, we obtain

$$n = 1: \quad \eta_0(t) = -1;$$

$$n = 2: \quad \eta_0(t) = e^{-0.2779t}\cos 0.4215t - 1 - 0.6594e^{-0.2779t}\sin 0.4215t,$$

$$\eta_1(t) = -0.6047e^{-0.2779t}\sin 0.4215t.$$

The respective approximate solutions can now be calculated from the formulas (26). Taking components along the x_0-axis and making use of the fact that $x_0 = x(t)$, we conclude that

$$n = 1: \quad x(t) \equiv 0;$$

$$n = 2: \quad x(t) = -78.48\eta_1(t).$$

Finally, on substituting the expression for $\eta_1(t)$, we end up with

$$n = 1 \quad x(t) \equiv 0;$$

$$n = 2 \quad x(t) = 47.46e^{-0.2779t}\sin 0.4215t.$$

For comparison sake, we give the exact solution of the differential equation (25):

$$x(t) = 0.164e^{-7.150t}\cos(3.35t + 0.732)$$
$$- 1.232e^{-0.648t}\cos(3.72t - 1.342)$$
$$+ 59.60e^{-0.377t}\cos(0.428t + 1.57).$$

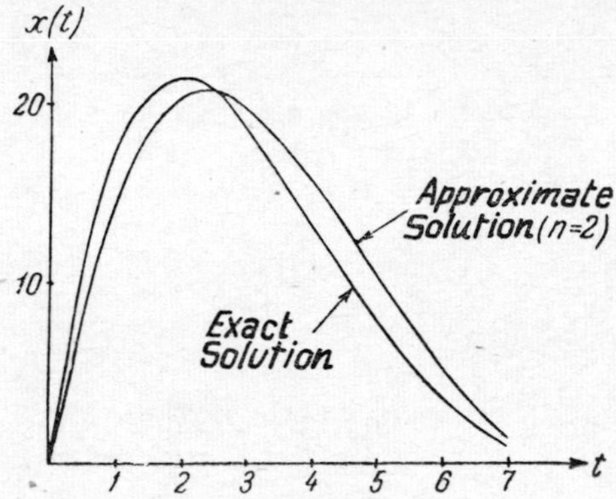

FIG. 8

Fig. 8 depicts the graphs of the second approximation and exact solution. It can be seen that for all practical purposes, the second approximation is already fully satisfactory.

CHAPTER VI

Generalization of the Method of Moments

I. Unbounded Operators

If a given operator is unbounded, any attempt to carry out the scheme of the method of moments immediately encounters a number of essential difficulties of a fundamental nature.

In view of the fact that such attempts have been undertaken without sufficient grounds (C. Lanczos), we felt it necessary to pause and consider the question.

Suppose A is an unbounded symmetric linear operator defined on a linear manifold L_A dense in the Hilbert space H. To formulate the problem of moments, we first of all have to have an element z_0 on which all powers of the operator A are defined. Generally speaking, no such element may exist. Nevertheless, we shall assume that it does. This will be the case, for example, if A has a simple spectrum. By solving the problem of moments, we can construct a sequence of operators A_n such that

$$\left.\begin{aligned} z_k = A^k z_0 &= A_n^k z_0 \quad (k = 0, 1, \ldots, n-1), \\ E_n z_n &= A_n^n z_0. \end{aligned}\right\}$$

Let us consider the linear manifold L_z of elements of the form

$$x = Q_m(A) z_0,$$

with Q_m any m-th degree polynomial. It is clear by definition of z_0 that all elements of L_z belong to the domain of definition of A, or in other words, $L_z \subset L_A$. Furthermore, the sequence of operators A_n converges (strongly) to A on the linear manifold L_z since for $n \geq m+1$

$$Ax = A_n x.$$

Thus, the limiting operator $A' = \lim_{n \to \infty} A_n$ coincides with A on the linear manifold L_z. If now $\bar{A}'$ the closure of A' is self-adjoint as is the original operator A, then according to a theorem of Rellich, the sequence of spectral functions corresponding to the operators A_n converges (strongly) to the spectral function of A at every point not belonging to the discrete spectrum of A. In this case, the problem of moments is said to be determinate. In the opposite case, we could not assert that the spectrum of A_n tends to a limit.

Thus, the solution of a problem with an unbounded operator by means of the method of moments involves considerable difficulties and is hardly reasonable even if the given operator is self-adjoint. First, it is usually rather difficult to construct an element z_0 on which all powers of the operator are defined. Second, even if such a z_0 were to be found, there would still be no certainty in being able to carry out the solution to the end since the problem of moments might turn out to be indeterminate.

These difficulties do not exist for bounded operators. They are defined everywhere, and we are therefore not bound in any way in our choice of z_0. As we have seen, it is usually natural to choose z_0 from the conditions of the specific problem. Moreover, the problem of moments is always defined for bounded operators and hence one is certain that the problem can be solved down to the end.

This raises the following question. Could not a problem involving an unbounded operator be reduced to a linear problem with a bounded operator? In certain cases, one can succeed in doing this.

Let A be a linear (unbounded) operator defined on a linear manifold L_A which is dense in the Hilbert space H. Consider the equation

$$Ax = f \tag{1}$$

and suppose the operator A is of the form

$$A = A_0 - K,$$

where A_0 is a positive definite self-adjoint operator defined on L_A. The conditions on the operator K will be presented below.

We define a new scalar product on the linear manifold L_A by means of the relation

$$[x, y] = (A_0 x, y).$$

Since A_0 is positive definite, a positive constant γ exists such that the inequality

$$[x, x] = (A_0 x, x) \geqq \gamma \| x \|^2 > 0, \quad x \neq 0,$$

holds for each $x \in L_A$.

The introduction of this new scalar product converts L_A into a Hilbert space, which, in general, is incomplete. By adjoining its ideal elements to it, we obtain a new space H_0. The linear manifold L_A is everywhere dense in H_0, and all elements of H_0 also belong to the given space H.

Now suppose that the operator K is such that $T = A_0^{-1} K$ is completely continuous in H_0 or more precisely, can be extended to be completely continuous. Then equation (1), i.e.,

$$A_0 x - K x = f \tag{1}$$

can be replaced by its equivalent

$$x - T x = A_0^{-1} f, \tag{2}$$

Which is already solvable by the method of moments.

We choose $A_0^{-1} f$ to be z_0 determining it from the equation

$$A_0 z_0 = f.$$

We then let $z_1 = T z_0 = A_0^{-1} K z_0$, and so

$$A_0 z_1 = K z_0.$$

In general, the elements in the sequence z_n are defined to be solutions of

$$A_0 z_k = K z_{k-1}.$$

When the coefficients of the polynomial $P_n(\lambda)$ are computed, it is of course necessary to take the scalar product of the new space H_0, that is,

$$[z_i, z_k] = (A_0 z_i, z_k) = (K z_{i-1}, z_k).$$

After this, the solution, if unique, may be found by the methods of Chapter II.

This procedure for solving equations can be used in practice only if the operator A_0 is of a sufficiently simple form and has been well analysed.

2. Generalized Method of Moments

The method of moments permits the determination of the spectrum of an operator in the subspace H_z, the completion of the linear manifold L_z consisting of elements of the form

$$x = Q_m(A)z_0,$$

where $Q_m(A)$ is an arbitrary polynomial. In general, H_z does not include the whole domain of the operator and depends on the choice of z_0. Thus, for example, as we have previously indicated, the operator A always has a simple spectrum in H_z and to each eigenvalue corresponds but one eigenelement. Let the given operator A be defined on the whole Hilbert space H and have multiple eigenvalues, that is, to certain of its eigenvalues there corresponds not one but an entire subspace of eigenelements. If the domain of definition of the operator is restricted to H_z, each eigenvalue loses its multiplicity and there exists just one eigenelement from out of the entire subspace. Moreover, in considering A in just the subspace H_z, we may lose not only eigenelements corresponding to multiple eigenvalues but even certain eigenvalues. Hence, it is of interest to generalize the method of moments in order to be able to treat operators in broader subspaces. This turns out to be useful in the solution of practical problems.

Let us consider the generalization of the problem of moments.

Let A be a bounded linear operator defined in the Hilbert space H. Our starting point is a set of m arbitrarily chosen linearly independent elements $z_0^{(1)}, z_0^{(2)}, \ldots, z_0^{(m)}$. We construct a sequence of iterations of each of these elements using the operator A as follows:

$$\left. \begin{aligned} z_0^{(1)}, \quad z_1^{(1)} &= A z_0^{(1)}, \ldots, z_{n_1}^{(1)} = A z_{n_1-1}^{(1)}, \ldots \\ \cdots\cdots\cdots\cdots\cdots\cdots\cdots\cdots\cdots\cdots\cdots\cdots \\ z_0^{(m)}, \quad z_1^{(m)} &= A z_0^{(m)}, \ldots, z_{n_m}^{(m)} = A z_{n_m-1}^{(m)}, \ldots \end{aligned} \right\} \tag{3}$$

The generalized problem of moments is the following:

To construct an operator $A_{n_1,n_2,\ldots,n_m}$ which is defined in the subspace $H_{n_1,n_2,\ldots,n_m}$ generated by all linear combinations of the elements

$$\left. \begin{aligned} z_0^{(1)}, \quad z_1^{(1)}, &\ldots, z_{n_1-1}^{(1)}, \\ \cdots\cdots\cdots\cdots\cdots \\ z_0^{(m)}, \quad z_1^{(m)}, &\ldots, z_{n_m-1}^{(m)}, \end{aligned} \right\} \tag{4}$$

and such that

$$
\left.
\begin{aligned}
z_k^{(1)} &= A_{n_1, n_2, \ldots, n_m}^k z_0^{(1)} \quad (k = 0, 1, \ldots, n_1 - 1), \\
E_{n_1, n_2, \ldots, n_m} z_{n_1}^{(1)} &= A_{n_1, n_2, \ldots, n_m}^{n_1} z_0^{(1)}, \\
& \cdot \quad \cdot \quad \cdot \quad \cdot \quad \cdot \quad \cdot \quad \cdot \quad \cdot \quad \cdot \quad \cdot \quad \cdot \quad \cdot \\
z_k^{(m)} &= A_{n_1, n_2, \ldots, n_m}^k z_0^{(m)} \quad (k = 0, 1, \ldots, n_m - 1), \\
E_{n_1, n_2, \ldots, n_m} z_{n_m}^{(m)} &= A_{n_1, n_2, \ldots, n_m}^{n_m} z_0^{(m)},
\end{aligned}
\right\} \tag{5}
$$

$E_{n_1, n_2, \ldots, n_m}$ being the operator projecting onto the subspace $H_{n_1, n_2, \ldots, n_m}$.

The problem of moments (5) has as its solution the operator determined by

$$
A_{n_1, n_2, \ldots, n_m} = E_{n_1, n_2, \ldots, n_m} A E_{n_1, n_2, \ldots, n_m}. \tag{6}
$$

If A is self-adjoint, then so is $A_{n_1, n_2, \ldots, n_m}$. Moreover, the sequence of operators $A_{n_1, n_2, \ldots, n_m}$ is uniformly bounded and

$$
\| A_{n_1, n_2, \ldots, n_m} \| \leq \| A \|.
$$

We then form the subspace $H_{z^{(1)}, z^{(2)}, \ldots, z^{(m)}}$ which is the completion of the linear manifold $L_{z^{(1)}, z^{(2)}, \ldots, z^{(m)}}$ generated by elements of the form

$$
x = Q_1(A) z_0^{(1)} + Q_2(A) z_0^{(2)} + \ldots + Q_m(A) z_0^{(m)},
$$

with the $Q_j(A)$ arbitrary polynomials.

In a manner quite similar to what was done before, it can be shown that the subspace $H_{z^{(1)}, z^{(2)}, \ldots, z^{(m)}}$ reduces the operator A and that the sequence $A_{n_1, n_2, \ldots, n_m}$ converges (strongly) to A in the subspace $H_{z^{(1)}, z^{(2)}, \ldots, z^{(m)}}$ when all subscripts tend to infinity.

If A is self-adjoint, this implies that the corresponding sequence of spectral functions converges (strongly):

$$
\mathscr{E}_\lambda^{n_1, \ldots, n_m} \to \mathscr{E}_\lambda \quad (n_1, n_2, \ldots, n_m \to \infty).
$$

And if A is completely continuous, the convergence is uniform and the eigenvalues of $A_{n_1, n_2, \ldots, n_m}$ converge to those of A.

We next show how the spectrum of the operator $A r_{1, n_2, \ldots, n_m}$ can be calculated. Suppose that the elements (3) forming a basis for the subspace $H_{n_1, n_2, \ldots, n_m}$ are linearly independent. Since $E_{n_1, n_2, \ldots, n_m} z_{n_j}^{(j)} \in H_{n_1, n_2, \ldots, n_m}$ $(j = 1, 2, \ldots, m)$, there exist numbers

$$
\alpha_{0j}^{(1)}, \ \alpha_{1j}^{(1)}, \ldots, \alpha_{n_1-1\,j}^{(1)}, \ \alpha_{0j}^{(2)}, \ \alpha_{1j}^{(2)}, \ldots, \alpha_{n_2-1\,j}^{(2)}, \ldots, \alpha_{0j}^{(m)}, \ \alpha_{1j}^{(m)}, \ldots, \alpha_{n_m-1\,j}^{(m)}
$$

$$
(j = 1, 2, \ldots, m),
$$

such that

$$E_{n_1,\ldots,n_m} z_{n_j}^{(j)} = -\alpha_{0j}^{(1)} z_0^{(1)} - \alpha_{1j}^{(1)} z_1^{(1)} - \ldots - \alpha_{n_1-1\,j}^{(1)} z_{n_1-1}^{(1)} - \alpha_{0j}^{(2)} z_0^{(2)}$$

$$-\alpha_{1j}^{(2)} z_1^{(2)} - \ldots - \alpha_{n_2-1\,j}^{(2)} z_{n_2-1}^{(2)} - \ldots - \alpha_{0j}^{(m)} z_0^{(m)}$$

$$-\alpha_{1j}^{(m)} z_1^{(m)} - \ldots - \alpha_{n_m-1\,j}^{(m)} z_{n_m-1}^{(m)} \quad (j=1,2,\ldots,m). \quad (7)$$

The scalar product of equation (7) with each of the basis elements (3) leads to a system of linear algebraic equations for the coefficients $\alpha_j^{(i)}$:

$$(z_0^{(1)}, z_s^{(k)})\alpha_{0j}^{(1)} + (z_1^{(1)}, z_s^{(k)})\alpha_{1j}^{(1)} + \ldots + (z_{n_1-1}^{(1)}, z_s^{(k)})\alpha_{n_1-1\,j}^{(1)}$$

$$+(z_0^{(2)}, z_s^{(k)})\alpha_{0j}^{(2)} + (z_1^{(2)}, z_s^{(k)})\alpha_{1j}^{(2)} + \ldots + (z_{n_2-1}^{(2)}, z_s^{(k)})\alpha_{n_2-1\,j}^{(2)} +$$

$$\cdot \quad \cdot \quad \cdot \quad \cdot \quad \cdot \quad \cdot \quad \cdot \quad \cdot \quad \cdot \quad \cdot \quad \cdot \quad \cdot \quad \cdot \quad \cdot$$

$$+(z_0^{(m)}, z_s^{(k)})\alpha_{0j}^{(m)} + (z_1^{(m)}, z_s^{(k)})\alpha_{1j}^{(m)} + \ldots$$

$$\ldots + (z_{n_m-1}^{(m)}, z_s^{(k)})\alpha_{n_m-1\,j}^{(m)} + (z_{n_j}^{(j)}, z_s^{(k)}) = 0$$

$$(j=1,2,\ldots,m; \; k=1,2,\ldots,m; \; s=0,1,\ldots,n_k-1). \quad (8)$$

Use of the relation

$$(E_{n_1,n_2,\ldots,n_m} z_{n_j}^{(j)}, z_s^{(k)}) = (z_{n_j}^{(j)}, z_s^{(k)}).$$

was made in obtaining this result.

The equations (8) actually comprise m systems of linear algebraic equations which differ only in their constant terms and which each are of order $n_1+n_2+\ldots+n_m$. The determinant of each system is the Gramian of the basis elements (3) and inasmuch as they have been assumed linearly independent, it does not vanish.

Suppose λ is an eigenvalue of $A_{n_1,n_2,\ldots,n_m}$ and u a corresponding eigenelement. Since $u \in H_{n_1,n_2,\ldots,n_m}$, it may be represented as

$$u = \sum_{j=1}^{m} (\xi_0^{(j)} z_0^{(j)} + \xi_1^{(j)} z_1^{(j)} + \ldots + \xi_{n_j-1}^{(j)} z_{n_j-1}^{(j)}).$$

Substituting this in the equation

$$A_{n_1,n_2,\ldots,n_m} u = \lambda u$$

and making use of (5) and (7), we obtain

$$\sum_{j=1}^{m} (\xi_0^{(j)} z_1^{(j)} + \xi_1^{(j)} z_2^{(j)} + \ldots + \xi_{n_j-2}^{(j)} z_{n_j-1}^{(j)}) - \sum_{j=1}^{m} \xi_{n_j-1}^{(j)} (\alpha_{0j}^{(1)} z_0^{(1)}$$

$$+\alpha_{1j}^{(1)} z_1^{(1)} + \ldots + \alpha_{n_1-1\,j}^{(1)} z_{n_1-1}^{(1)} + \alpha_{0j}^{(2)} z_0^{(2)} + \alpha_{1j}^{(2)} z_1^{(2)} + \ldots$$

$$\ldots + \alpha_{n_2-1\,j}^{(2)} z_{n_2-1}^{(2)} + \ldots + \alpha_{0j}^{(m)} z_0^{(m)} + \alpha_{1j}^{(m)} z_1^{(m)} + \ldots$$

$$\ldots + \alpha_{n_m-1\,j}^{(m)} z_{n_m-1}^{(m)}) = \lambda \sum_{j=1}^{m} (\xi_0^{(j)} z_0^{(j)} + \xi_1^{(j)} z_1^{(j)} + \ldots + \xi_{n_j-1}^{(j)} z_{n_j-1}^{(j)}).$$

Equating coefficients of like terms, we arrive at a system of equations for the $\xi_s^{(j)}$ and λ:

$$\left.\begin{array}{c} -\sum_{j=1}^{m} \xi_{n_j-1}^{(j)} \alpha_{0j}^{(k)} = \lambda \xi_0^{(k)}, \\[2mm] \xi_0^{(k)} - \sum_{j=1}^{m} \xi_{n_j-1}^{(j)} \alpha_{1j}^{(k)} = \lambda \xi_1^{(k)}, \\[2mm] \cdot \quad \cdot \quad \cdot \quad \cdot \quad \cdot \quad \cdot \quad \cdot \quad \cdot \quad \cdot \quad \cdot \\[2mm] \xi_{n_k-2}^{(k)} - \sum_{j=1}^{m} \xi_{n_j-1}^{(j)} \alpha_{n_k-1\,j}^{(k)} = \lambda \xi_{n_k-1}^{(k)} \end{array}\right\} \quad (k = 1, 2, \ldots, m). \quad (9)$$

The eigenvalues of $A_{n_1,n_2,\ldots,n_m}$ are roots of the determinant of the system (9). The solution of the latter also yields the coefficients $\xi_s^{(j)}$.

Till now, we have assumed that the elements of the sequence (3) are all linearly independent. If this is not so, and some of the elements of the sequence (3) are linearly dependent on the others, the procedure for constructing the subspace $H_{z^{(1)},z^{(2)},\ldots,z^{(m)}}$ has to be slightly modified. Suppose for definiteness that in the iteration process, the element $z_{n_j}^{(j)}$ turns out to be linearly dependent on the elements $z_0^{(1)},\ldots,z_{n_1-1}^{(1)}$, $\ldots,z_0^{(m)},\ldots,z_{n_m-1}^{(m)}$. In our notation, this can be expressed by the relation

$$E_{n_1,\,n_2,\,\ldots,\,n_m} z_{n_j}^{(j)} = z_{n_j}^{(j)}.$$

In that case, no further iterations of $z_{n_j}^{(j)}$ by A need be carried out, and the subspace $H_{z^{(1)},z^{(2)},\ldots,z^{(m)}}$ is the completion of the linear manifold $L_{z^{(1)},z^{(2)},\ldots,z^{(m)}}$ consisting of elements of the form

$$x = Q_1(A)z_0^{(1)} + \ldots + Q_j(A)z_0^{(j)} + \ldots + Q_m(A)z_0^{(m)},$$

where the degree of the polynomial $Q_j(A)$ is no higher than $n_j - 1$. The subspace $H_{z^{(1)},z^{(2)},\ldots,z^{(m)}}$ also reduces the operator A in the present case.

Moreover, if for certain values of $n_1,n_2,\ldots,n_m$ the elements $z_{n_1}^{(1)},\ldots,z_{n_m}^{(1)}$ can all be expressed as linear combinations of the preceding elements and also belong to $H_{n_1,n_2,\ldots,n_m}$, then $H_{z^{(1)},z^{(2)},\ldots,z^{(m)}}$ reduces A and coincides with $H_{n_1,n_2,\ldots,n_m}$. A and $A_{n_1,n_2,\ldots,n_m}$ are equivalent operators in this subspace.

The generalized method of moments may be of use not only in computing the spectrum of operators in broader subspaces but also in solving linear problems.

We are not going to discuss all possible applications of the generalized method of moments. Our illustration of it will be confined to just one example.

Consider the equation

$$\frac{\partial x}{\partial t} = -Ax + g_1 f_1(t) + g_2 f_2(t) + \ldots + g_{m-1} f_{m-1}(t), \qquad (10)$$

where $g_1, \ldots, g_{m-1}$ are prescribed elements of the Hilbert space H, A is a positive definite symmetric operator (unbounded, generally speaking), $x \in H$ is the required solution, and $f_1(t), f_2(t), \ldots, f_{m-1}(t)$ are scalar functions.

The solution is completely determined by assigning initial data, say, $x = x_0$ at $t = 0$.

Since A is positive definite, it has a bounded inverse, which we shall assume to be defined on the whole of H.

We rewrite equation (10) in the form

$$A^{-1} \frac{\partial x}{\partial t} + x = A^{-1} g_1 f_1(t) + \ldots + A^{-1} g_{m-1} f_{m-1}(t). \qquad (10')$$

This equation could be solved by the method of moments by expressing the required solution in the form

$$x = x_0(t) + x_1(t) + \ldots + x_{m-1}(t),$$

where the $x_k(t)$ are solutions of the equations

$$A^{-1} \frac{\partial x_0(t)}{\partial t} + x_0(t) = 0, \quad x_0(0) = x_0,$$

$$A^{-1} \frac{\partial x_k(t)}{\partial t} + x_k(t) = A^{-1} g_k f_k(t), \quad x_k(0) = 0.$$

Ways of solving these equations by the method of moments were discussed in Chapter V.

If we introduce the notation

$$z_0^{(1)} = x_0, \quad z_0^{(2)} = g_1, \ldots, z_0^{(m)} = g_{m-1},$$

it is easy to see that $x_k(t)$ belongs to the subspace $H_{z^{(k)}}$ formed by completing the linear manifold consisting of elements of the form

$$x_k = Q(A) z_0^{(k)}.$$

In general, the subspaces $H_{z^{(k)}}$ overlap one another and some of them may simply coincide. Therefore, it is natural to look at once for a solution in the subspace $H_{z^{(1)}, z^{(2)}, \ldots, z^{(m)}}$ which contains all the subspaces $H_{z^{(k)}}$. To this end, we have to apply the generalized method of moments.

We first compute the set of basis elements (3) with the role of A in these formulas taken by the inverse operator A^{-1}. We have

$$z_0^{(1)} = x_0, \quad z_1^{(1)} = A^{-1}z_0^{(1)}, \ldots, z_{n_1}^{(1)} = A^{-1}z_{n_1-1}^{(1)},$$

. . . .

$$z_0^{(m)} = g_{m-1}, \quad z_1^{(m)} = A^{-1}z_0^{(m)}, \ldots, z_{n_m}^{(m)} = A^{-1}z_{n_m-1}^{(m)}.$$

The elements $z_s^{(k)}$ are then determined recursively from the relations

$$Az_1^{(1)} = z_0^{(1)} = x_0, \ldots, Az_{n_1}^{(1)} = z_{n_1-1}^{(1)},$$

. . . .

$$Az_1^{(m)} = z_0^{(m)} = g_{m-1}, \ldots, Az_{n_m}^{(m)} = z_{n_m-1}^{(m)}.$$

We next replace equation (10′) by the close equation

$$A_{n_1, n_2, \ldots, n_m} \frac{\partial x_{n_1, \ldots, n_m}}{\partial t} + x_{n_1, \ldots, n_m} = z_1^{(2)}f_1(t) + \ldots + z_1^{(m)}f_{m-1}(t). \quad (11)$$

It is easy to show that the sequence $x_{n_1, n_2, \ldots, n_m}$ converges to the required solution x when the subscripts all tend to infinity provided we let $x_{n_1, n_2, \ldots, n_m}(0) = x_0$.

Since A^{-1} is self-adjoint, we may take advantage of its spectral representation

$$A^{-1} = \int_0^M \lambda \, d\mathscr{E}_\lambda, \quad M > 0.$$

The required solution can be shown by direct verification to be expressible as follows:

$$x = \int_0^M e^{-t/\lambda} d\mathscr{E}_\lambda x_0 + \sum_{j=1}^{m-1} \int_0^M \left[\int_0^t f_j(\xi)e^{-(t-\xi)/\lambda} d\xi \right] d\mathscr{E}_\lambda g_j.$$

Now, A^{-1} is a positive operator, while $e^{-t/\lambda}$ and

$$\int_0^t f_j(\xi)e^{-1/\lambda(t-\xi)} \, d\xi$$

are continuous functions for positive values of λ. Therefore, the fact the sequence $A_{n_1, n_2, \ldots, n_m}$ converges strongly to A implies the sequence $x_{n_1, n_2, \ldots, n_m}$ converges strongly to x when all subscripts tend to infinity.

Let us next show how the approximate solutions may be calculated. Since $x_{n_1,n_2,\ldots,n_m}$ belongs to the subspace $H_{n_1,n_2,\ldots,n_m}$, it can be represented as

$$x_{n_1,\ldots,n_m} = \sum_{j=1}^{m} \left[z_0^{(j)}\eta_0^{(j)}(t) + z_1^{(j)}\eta_1^{(j)}(t) + \ldots + z_{n_j-1}^{(j)}\eta_{n_j-1}^{(j)}(t) \right],$$

where the $\eta_k^{(j)}(t)$ are scalar functions of time.

Substituting this expression in (11) and making use of (5), we obtain

$$\sum_{j=1}^{m} \left(z_1^{(j)} \frac{d\eta_0^{(j)}}{dt} + z_2^{(j)} \frac{d\eta_1^{(j)}}{dt} + \ldots + z_{n_j-1}^{(j)} \frac{d\eta_{n_j-2}^{(j)}}{dt} \right)$$

$$+ \sum_{j=1}^{m} E_{n_1,\ldots,n_m} z_{n_j}^{(j)} \frac{d\eta_{n_j-1}^{(j)}}{dt} + \sum_{j=1}^{m} (z_0^{(j)}\eta_0^{(j)} + z_1^{(j)}\eta_1^{(j)} + \ldots$$

$$\ldots + z_{n_j-1}^{(j)}\eta_{n_j-1}^{(j)}) = \sum_{j=2}^{m} z_1^{(j)} f_{j-1}(t).$$

The application of (7) and the equating of coefficients of like terms then leads to a system of ordinary differential equations for the functions $\eta_k^{(s)}(t)$, namely,

$$\eta_0^{(s)} - \sum_{j=1}^{m} \alpha_{0j}^{(s)} \frac{d\eta_{n_j-1}^{(j)}}{dt} = 0,$$

$$\frac{d\eta_0^{(s)}}{dt} + \eta_1^{(s)} - \sum_{j=1}^{m} \alpha_{1j}^{(s)} \frac{d\eta_{n_j-1}^{(j)}}{dt} = f_{s-1}(t),$$

$$\frac{d\eta_1^{(s)}}{dt} + \eta_2^{(s)} - \sum_{j=1}^{m} \alpha_{2j}^{(s)} \frac{d\eta_{n_j-1}^{(j)}}{dt} = 0,$$

$$\cdot \quad \cdot \quad \cdot \quad \cdot \quad \cdot \quad \cdot \quad \cdot \quad \cdot \quad \cdot \quad \cdot \quad \cdot$$

$$\frac{d\eta_{n_s-2}^{(s)}}{dt} + \eta_{n_s-1}^{(s)} - \sum_{j=1}^{m} \alpha_{n_s-1\,j}^{(s)} \frac{d\eta_{n_j-1}^{(j)}}{dt} = 0$$

$$(s = 1, 2, \ldots, m).$$

In this, $f_0(t)$ is understood to be zero. Moreover, if $x_{n_1,n_2,\ldots,n_m}$ is to satisfy the stated initial condition, then it is necessary that

$$\eta_0^{(1)}(0) = 1, \quad \eta_1^{(1)}(0) = \ldots = \eta_{n_1-1}^{(1)}(0) =$$

$$\ldots = \eta_0^{(m)}(0) = \ldots = \eta_{n_m-1}^{(m)}(0) = 0.$$

These initial conditions assure the uniqueness of the solution.

CHAPTER VII

Solution of Integral and Differential Equations

I. Integral Equations

Consider the real integral equation

$$x(s) = \mu \int_a^b K(s,t)x(t)\,dt + f(s) \qquad (1)$$

and introduce the Hilbert space L_2 of square integrable functions $x(s)$ defined on the interval $[a,b]$. The scalar product and norm in L_2 are given by

$$(x,y) = \int_a^b x(t)y(t)\,dt, \quad \|x\| = \sqrt{\int_a^b x^2(t)\,dt}.$$

If the operator A defined by

$$Ax = \int_a^b K(s,t)x(t)\,dt,$$

is introduced, equation (1) can be written in the form

$$x = \mu Ax + f. \qquad (2)$$

The operator A is completely continuous if the double integral of the kernel squared exists, i.e.,

$$\int_a^b \int_a^b K^2(s,t)\,ds\,dt < \infty,$$

and

$$\|A\|^2 \leq \int_a^b \int_a^b K^2(s,t)\,ds\,dt.$$

One of the topics in the classical theory of integral equations is usually the Liouville-Neumann method in which a solution of (1) is sought as a power series in the parameter μ:

$$x(s) = z_0(s) + \mu z_1(s) + \mu^2 z_2(s) + \ldots + \mu^n z_n(s) + \ldots .$$

Here,

$$z_0(s) = f(s), \quad z_1(s) = A z_0 = \int_a^b K(s,t) f(t)\, dt, \ldots$$

$$\ldots, z_n(s) = A z_{n-1} = \int_a^b K(s,t) z_{n-1}(t)\, dt, \ldots .$$

It is shown that the series converges to $x(s)$ in the mean whenever

$$|\mu|^2 < \frac{1}{\displaystyle\int_a^b \int_a^b K^2(s,t)\, ds\, dt}. \tag{3}$$

In the method of moments, we look for an approximate solution of a slightly more general form

$$x_n(s) = a_0(\mu) z_0(s) + a_1(\mu) z_1(s) + \ldots + a_{n-1}(\mu) z_{n-1}(s), \tag{4}$$

where the coefficients a_k are found from the following formulas:

$$\left.\begin{aligned} a_0 &= 1 - \frac{\alpha_0}{P_n\!\left(\dfrac{1}{\mu}\right)}, \\[2ex] a_1 &= \mu a_0 - \frac{\alpha_1}{P_n\!\left(\dfrac{1}{\mu}\right)}, \\[1ex] &\cdot \quad \cdot \quad \cdot \quad \cdot \\[1ex] a_{n-1} &= \mu a_{n-2} - \frac{\alpha_n - 1}{P_n\!\left(\dfrac{1}{\mu}\right)}, \end{aligned}\right\}$$

$$\left.\begin{aligned} (z_0, z_0)\alpha_0 + (z_0, z_1)\alpha_1 + \ldots + (z_0, z_{n-1})\alpha_{n-1} + (z_0, z_n) &= 0, \\ (z_1, z_0)\alpha_0 + (z_1, z_1)\alpha_1 + \ldots + (z_1, z_{n-1})\alpha_{n-1} + (z_1, z_n) &= 0, \\ \cdot \quad \cdot \quad \cdot \quad \cdot \quad \cdot \quad \cdot \quad \cdot \quad \cdot \quad \cdot \quad \cdot \quad \cdot \quad \cdot \\ (z_{n-1}, z_0)\alpha_0 + (z_{n-1}, z_1)\alpha_1 + \ldots + (z_{n-1}, z_{n-1})\alpha_{n-1} + (z_{n-1}, z_n) &= 0, \end{aligned}\right\} \tag{5}$$

$$P_n(\lambda) = \lambda^n + \alpha_{n-1}\lambda^{n-1} + \ldots + \alpha_0,$$

$$(z_i, z_k) = \int_a^b z_i(t) z_k(t)\, dt.$$

The sequence $x_n(s)$ converges in the mean to the solution, namely,

$$\int_a^b [x(s) - x_n(s)]^2 ds \to 0$$

not only under the condition (3) but also for every regular value of μ, i.e., when a solution to (1) exists for any choice of $f(s)$ in L_2.

The determination of the approximate solution $x_n(s)$ is greatly simplified whenever the kernel is symmetric. In this case one can usually make use of the algorithm (36′) of Chapter III:

$$x_{n+1}(s) = x_n(s) + h_n g_n(s),$$

$$g_n(s) = r_n(s) + l_{n-1} g_{n-1}(s),$$

$$r_n(s) = r_{n-1}(s) - h_{n-1}\left[g_{n-1}(s) - \mu \int_a^b K(s,t) g_{n-1}(t) dt \right], \qquad (6)$$

$$h_n = \frac{\displaystyle\int_a^b r_n^2(s)\, ds}{\displaystyle\int_b^b \left[g_n(s) - \mu \int_a^b K(s,t) g_n(t)\, dt \right] g_n(s)\, ds},$$

$$l_n = \frac{\displaystyle\int_a^b r_{n+1}^2(s)\, ds}{\displaystyle\int_a^b r_n^2(s)\, ds},$$

$$r_0(s) = g_0(s) = f(s),$$

$$r_n(s) = f(s) - x_n(s) + \mu \int_a^b K(s,t) x_n(t)\, dt.$$

If the condition (3) holds, $I - \mu A$ is a positive definite operator, $x_n(s)$ exists for all values of n, and the sequence $x_n(s)$ converges in the mean to the solution of equation (1). But if the condition is not satisfied, then in these exceptional cases, h_n can become infinite for certain values of n, and it is then necessary to resort to the method presented in Chapter III.

As has already been shown, $x_n(s)$ approaches the solution faster than any geometric progression.

The solution of an integral equation by the method of moments involves a great number of quadratures. Therefore, it sometimes turns out to be more expedient to take for the initial element z_0 not the function $f(s)$ in the integral equation but some other function for which the quadratures can easily be performed and such that $f(s)$ can be approximated by functions of the form

$$\phi(s) = a_0 z_0 + a_1 z_1 + \ldots + a_n z_n + \ldots$$

to any desired degree of accuracy. The solution of the integral equation can then be obtained using the formulas of Chapters II and III.

We note that it is often more effective to apply the method of moments not alone but in conjunction with an iterative process.

2. Boundary Value Problems for Ordinary Differential Equations

Let us next consider a second order linear differential equation

$$Ax = \frac{d}{dt}[p(t)x'(t)] + \frac{d}{dt}[q(t)x(t)] + r(t)x(t) = f(t), \tag{7}$$

with

$$x(0) = x(1) = 0, \quad p(t) > 0, \quad 0 \le t \le 1.$$

Let

$$Ax = A_0 x + Kx,$$

where

$$A_0 x = \frac{d}{dt}[p(t)x'(t)], \quad Kx = \frac{d}{dt}[q(t)x(t)] + r(t)x(t).$$

The operator A_0 is negative definite on the linear manifold L_A of functions defined on the interval $[0,1]$ having continuous derivatives up to second order inclusive and equal to zero at the endpoints of the interval. For,

$$-(A_0 x, x) = -\int_0^1 \frac{d}{dt}(px')x \, dt = \int_0^1 p(t)x'^2(t) \, dt$$

$$\ge \min p(t) \int_0^1 x'^2(t) \, dt \ge \frac{\min p(t)}{\pi^2} \int_0^1 x^2(t) \, dt = \frac{\min p(t)}{\pi^2} \| x \|^2.$$

We now introduce a new space H_0 in which the scalar product is defined by

$$[x, y] = -(A_0 x, y) = -\int_0^1 \frac{d}{dt}(px')y \, dt = \int_0^1 p(t)x'(t)y'(t) \, dt.$$

Let us show that $A_0^{-1}K$ is a completely continuous operator in H_0. To this end, we introduce a Green's function such that

$$v = A_0^{-1}u = \int_0^1 G(s,t)u(t)\,dt.$$

Therefore,

$$y = A_0^{-1}Kx = \int_0^1 G(s,t)\left[\frac{d}{dt}(qx)+rx\right]dt.$$

Since G has continuous first derivatives (except for a finite jump at $s=t$), we have

$$y'(s) = \int_0^1 \frac{\partial G(s,t)}{\partial s}\left[\frac{d}{dt}(qx)+rx\right]dt.$$

If the differentiation of the product is carried out and the terms involving $x(t)$ are integrated by parts, there results

$$y'(s) = \int_0^1 N(s,t)x'(t)\,dt, \tag{8}$$

where $\qquad N(s,t) = \dfrac{\partial G(s,t)}{\partial s}q(t)-\displaystyle\int_0^t \dfrac{\partial G(s,\xi)}{\partial s}\left[q'(\xi)+r(\xi)\right]d\xi.$

The function $N(s,t)$ is continuous (except for a finite jump at $s=t$) and so the expression (8) defines a completely continuous transformation. Hence, $A^{-1}K$ is completely continuous.

Thus, if equation (7) has a unique solution, it can be found by the method of moments.

The initial function $z_0(t)$ is the solution of the boundary-value problem

$$\frac{d}{dt}[p(t)z_0'(t)] = f(t), \quad z_0(0) = z_0(1) = 0.$$

Hence $\quad z_0(t) = \displaystyle\int_0^t \frac{1}{p(\xi)}\int_0^\xi f(\eta)\,d\eta\,d\xi - \frac{\displaystyle\int_0^1 \frac{1}{p(\xi)}\int_0^\xi f(\eta)\,d\eta\,d\xi}{\displaystyle\int_0^1 \frac{d\xi}{p(\xi)}}\int_0^t \frac{d\xi}{p(\xi)}.$

The remaining terms in the sequence z_k are determined recursively from the equation

$$A_0 z_k = Kz_{k-1},$$

or explicitly,

$$\frac{d}{dt}[p(t)z_k'(t)] = \frac{d}{dt}[q(t)z_{k-1}(t)] + r(t)z_{k-1}(t).$$

under the conditions $z_k(0) = z_k(1) = 0$. In the present instance,

$$[z_i, z_k] = -(A_0 z_i, z_k) = -(Kz_{i-1}, z_k) = -\int_0^1 \left[\frac{d}{dt}(qz_{i-1}) + rz_{i-1}\right]z_k dt.$$

The balance of the solution computation proceeds according to the usual scheme. Replacing equation (7) by its equivalent

$$x(t) + Tx(t) = A_0^{-1}f(t) = z_0(t), \qquad (9)$$

with $T = A_0^{-1}K$, and making use of the fact that

$$z_k = Tz_{k-1},$$

we find the solution by the method of Chapter II.

We merely note that the sequence of approximations converges in the mean in H_0, that is,

$$-\int_0^1 \frac{d}{dt}[p(t)(x' - x_n')](x - x_n)\,dt = \int_0^1 p(t)(x' - x_n')^2\,dt \to 0.$$

And hence, the fact that $p(t)$ is positive implies that the approximations $x_n(t)$ converge uniformly to the solution of equation (7).

We proceed now to consider the eigenvalue problem.

Since a differential operator is unbounded, the method of moments cannot, generally speaking, be applied directly to determine its spectrum. However, if such an operator is self-adjoint so that

$$A = \int_{-\infty}^{\infty} \lambda\,d\mathscr{E}_\lambda,$$

then its spectrum can be found by applying the method of moments to some bounded operator

$$f(A) = \int_{-\infty}^{\infty} f(\lambda)\,d\mathscr{E}_\lambda,$$

where the function $f(\lambda)$ is bounded on the spectrum of A. After the eigenvalues of the operator $f(A)$ have been computed (the corresponding equation is $f(A)u = \mu u$), those of the given operator A are easily obtained from the relation

$$f(\lambda) = \mu.$$

On the other hand, the eigenelements of A and $f(A)$ are the same.

For illustrative purposes, consider the Sturm-Liouville problem

$$-\frac{d}{dt}\left[p(t)\frac{du}{dt}\right]+q(t)u(t) = \lambda r(t)u(t), \qquad \left.\begin{array}{l}\\[2mm]\\\end{array}\right\} \tag{10}$$
$$u'(a)-\alpha u(a) = 0, \quad u'(b)+\beta u(b) = 0,$$

with $p(t)$ and $r(t)$ strictly positive, continuous functions of t on the interval $a \leqq t \leqq b$.

The operator

$$Au = \frac{1}{r(t)}\left[-\frac{d}{dt}\left[p(t)\frac{du}{dt}\right]+q(t)u(t)\right]$$

is unbounded, and its spectrum consists of real eigenvalues, the negative ones being finite in number. Suppose l is a real number equal to none of the eigenvalues of equation (10). Then the operator $B = (A-lI)^{-1}$ is bounded, self-adjoint, and even completely continuous. The method of moments can therefore be applied to determine its spectrum.

We first show how to compute the sequence z_k. For $z_0(t)$, any square integrable function will suffice. We define

$$z_1(t) = Bz_0(t)$$

or

$$(A-lI)z_1 = z_0.$$

Thus $z_1(t)$ is a solution of the boundary value problem

$$-\frac{d}{dt}\left[p(t)\frac{sz_1(t)}{dt}\right]+q(t)z_1(t)-lr(t)z_1(t) = r(t)z_0(t), \qquad \left.\begin{array}{l}\\[2mm]\\\end{array}\right\} \tag{11}$$
$$z_1'(a)-\alpha z_1(a) = 0, \quad z_1'(b)+\beta z_1(b) = 0.$$

The other terms in the sequence are defined recursively in a similar way by

$$(A-lI)z_k(t) = z_{k-1}(t). \tag{11'}$$

As for the scalar product, it is convenient to take it to be

$$(z_i, z_k) = \int_a^b r(t) z_i(t) z_k(t) \, dt.$$

The rest of the spectral computation for the operator B proceeds as usual. We let

$$Bu = \mu u.$$

Then $u(t)$ is a solution of (10), and the eigenvalues of A are given by

$$\lambda = \frac{1}{\mu} + l.$$

As was noted on an earlier occasion, the method of moments permits us to calculate with the greatest of accuracy the eigenvalues of an operator that are largest in absolute value. Since $\mu = (\lambda - l)^{-1}$, the eigenvalues of B largest in absolute value correspond to those values of λ close to l. Thus, by varying l, we can find the eigenvalues and eigenfunctions associated with any range of the spectrum of the differential equation (10) that concerns us.

It is also possible to compute in this way the eigenvalues of a non-self-adjoint differential equation provided only that the operator A^{-1} is completely continuous.

The above method of obtaining the eigenvalues entails solving the differential equations (11) and (11′). It therefore sometimes turns out to be more expedient to define the operator B differently.

We introduce a fictitious partial differential equation and conditions

$$\left.\begin{array}{c} \dfrac{\partial}{\partial t}\left[p(t) \dfrac{\partial v(t, \xi)}{\partial t} \right] - q(t) v(t, \xi) = r(t) \dfrac{\partial v(t, \xi)}{\partial \xi}, \\[2mm] \dfrac{\partial v}{\partial t} - \alpha v \bigg|_{t=a} = 0, \quad \dfrac{\partial v}{\partial t} + \beta v \bigg|_{t=b} = 0, \\[2mm] v(t, 0) = z_0(t) \end{array}\right\} \tag{12}$$

and assume that its solution has been found by any one of the numerical methods for $\xi = h, \ \xi = 2h, \ldots, \ \xi = nh, \ldots$.

We rewrite equation (12) in operator form obtaining

$$-Av = \frac{\partial v}{\partial \xi}, \qquad v = z_0(t), \quad \xi = 0.$$

The integration of this equation yields

$$v(t, \xi) = \int_{-\infty}^{\infty} e^{-\lambda \xi} d\mathscr{E}_\lambda z_0 = e^{-A\xi} z_0,$$

so that

$$\left. \begin{aligned} v(t, 0) &= z_0(t), \\ v(t, h) &= \int_{-\infty}^{\infty} e^{-\lambda h} d\mathscr{E}_\lambda z_0, \\ &\quad \cdot \quad \cdot \quad \cdot \quad \cdot \quad \cdot \quad \cdot \quad \cdot \quad \cdot \\ v(t, nh) &= \int_{-\infty}^{\infty} e^{-nh\lambda} d\mathscr{E}_\lambda z_0. \end{aligned} \right\} \tag{13}$$

We now define B by the formula $B = e^{-hA}$. Since A has a finite number of negative eigenvalues, B is bounded.

From (13), we see that

$$v(t, 0) = z_0(t),$$

$$v(t, h) = z_1(t) = Bz_0(t),$$

$$\cdot \quad \cdot \quad \cdot \quad \cdot \quad \cdot \quad \cdot \quad \cdot \quad \cdot$$

$$v(t, nh) = z_n(t) = B^n z_0(t).$$

Thus, by solving the fictitious equation (12), we have obtained the indicated set of powers of the bounded operator B.

The eigenvalues and eigenfunctions of B are now found by solving the problem of moments in the usual manner. Let

$$Bu = \mu u.$$

Then u is a solution of (10) corresponding to the eigenvalue λ given by

$$\lambda = -\frac{1}{h} \ln \mu.$$

Another slightly different way of setting up the fictitious partial differential equation is given by Milne (1). He uses

$$-\frac{\partial}{\partial t}\left[p(t)\frac{\partial v(t,\xi)}{\partial t}\right]+q(t)v(t,\xi)=r(t)\frac{\partial^2 v(t,\xi)}{\partial \xi^2},$$

$$\left.\frac{\partial v}{\partial t}-\alpha v\right|_{t=a}=0,\quad \left.\frac{\partial v}{\partial t}+\beta v\right|_{t=b}=0,$$

$$v(t,0)=z_0(t),\quad \frac{\partial v(t,0)}{\partial \xi}=0.$$

$$(14)$$

When (14) is solved, there results

$$v(t,\xi)=\int_{-\infty}^{\infty}\cos\xi\sqrt{\lambda}\,d\mathscr{E}_\lambda z_0,$$

$$v(t,0)=z_0(t),$$

$$v(t,h)=\int_{-\infty}^{\infty}\cos h\sqrt{\lambda}\,d\mathscr{E}_\lambda z_0,$$

$$\cdot \quad \cdot \quad \cdot \quad \cdot \quad \cdot \quad \cdot \quad \cdot \quad \cdot \quad \cdot \quad \cdot \quad \cdot \quad \cdot$$

$$v(t,nh)=\int_{-\infty}^{\infty}\cos nh\sqrt{\lambda}\,d\mathscr{E}_\lambda z_0.$$

$$(15)$$

Now define a bounded operator B by the formula

$$B=\int_{-\infty}^{\infty}\cos h\sqrt{\lambda}\,d\mathscr{E}_\lambda.$$

The powers of this operator are easily calculated by making use of the identity

$$\cos^k\sqrt{\lambda}=(\tfrac{1}{2})^{k-1}\left[\cos k\sqrt{\lambda}+\binom{k}{1}\cos(k-2)\sqrt{\lambda}+\ldots+\binom{k}{\frac{k-1}{2}}\cos\sqrt{\lambda}\right]$$

for odd k and the identity

$$\cos^k\sqrt{\lambda}=(\tfrac{1}{2})^{k-1}\left[\cos k\sqrt{\lambda}\right.$$

$$\left.+\binom{k}{1}\cos(k-2)\sqrt{\lambda}+\ldots+\binom{k}{\frac{k-2}{2}}\cos 2\sqrt{\lambda}\right]+\binom{k}{\frac{k}{2}}\frac{1}{2^k}$$

for even k. In fact,

$$z_1(t) = Bz_0 = v(t,h),$$

$$z_2(t) = B^2 z_0 = \int_{-\infty}^{\infty} \cos^2 h \sqrt{\lambda} \, d\mathscr{E}_\lambda z_0 = \tfrac{1}{2} \int_{-\infty}^{\infty} d\mathscr{E}_\lambda z_0$$

$$+ \tfrac{1}{2} \int_{-\infty}^{\infty} \cos 2h \sqrt{\lambda} \, d\mathscr{E}_\lambda z_0 = \tfrac{1}{2} z_0(t) + \tfrac{1}{2} v(t, 2h),$$

. . . .

$$z_k(t) = B^k z_0 = \begin{cases} \dfrac{1}{2^{k-1}} \left[v(t,kh) + \dbinom{k}{1} v[t,(k-2)h] + \ldots \right. \\ \qquad\qquad \left. \ldots + \dbinom{k}{\frac{k-1}{2}} v(t,h) \right] \quad \text{(odd } k\text{)}, \\[2em] \dfrac{1}{2^{k-1}} \left[v(t,kh) + \dbinom{k}{1} v[t,(k-2)h] + \ldots \right. \\ \qquad \left. \ldots + \dbinom{k}{\frac{k-2}{2}} v(t,2h) \right] + \dbinom{k}{\frac{k}{2}} \dfrac{z_0(t)}{2^k} \quad \text{(even } k\text{)}. \end{cases}$$

The spectrum of B can now be found by the usual scheme of the method of moments.

After the eigenvalues μ of B have been calculated, it is a simple matter to find those of the given equation (10) by the use of

$$\lambda h^2 = [\text{arc} \cos \mu]^2.$$

To solve the equation (14), Milne recommends the use of the method of finite differences.

3. Partial Differential Equations with Variable Coefficients

We next consider the solution of the boundary value problem of the first kind for the following elliptic equation with variable coefficients:

$$Au = a(x, y)\frac{\partial^2 u}{\partial x^2} + b(x, y)\frac{\partial^2 u}{\partial y^2} + c(x, y)\frac{\partial u}{\partial x}$$

$$+ d(x, y)\frac{\partial u}{\partial y} - g(x, y)u = f(x, y). \quad (16)$$

Here, a, b, c, d, g, and f are continuous on some finite domain D, a and b are positive, and g is non-negative. On the boundary Γ of D, we suppose for simplicity that $u = 0$. The operator is defined on the linear manifold L_A of functions having continuous derivatives up to second order inclusive in D and equal to zero on the boundary. We define the scalar product on the linear manifold L_A to be

$$(u, v) = \iint_D u\, v d\sigma.$$

Let the operator

$$A_0 u = -a_0 \frac{\partial^2 u}{\partial x^2} - b_0 \frac{\partial^2 u}{\partial y^2} + g_0 u,$$

with a_0, b_0 positive constants and g_0 a non-negative constant, be defined on this same linear manifold. A_0 is positive definite.

The introduction of a new scalar product $[u, v] = (A_0 u, v)$ and the completion of L_A then results in a Hilbert space, which we denote by H_0.

If we apply A_0^{-1} to both sides of (16), we arrive at the operator equation

$$A_0^{-1} Au = A_0^{-1} f, \quad (17)$$

with an operator $A_0^{-1} A$ bounded in H_0.

In general, the method of moments may be applied to solve (17). The convergence of the resultant approximations can easily be established if, for example, A is negative definite or if a and b are positive constants. In the first case, $A_0^{-1} A$ is self-adjoint and negative definite in H_0, while in the second case, it can be represented as the sum of the identity operator and a completely continuous operator in H_0.

To solve equation (17) by the method of moments, it is first necessary to form the sequence of functions

$$z_0 = A_0^{-1} f, \qquad z_1 = A_0^{-1} A z_0, \dots$$

which are determinable from the recursive differential equations

$$-a_0 \frac{\partial^2 z_0}{\partial x^2} - b_0 \frac{\partial^2 z_0}{\partial y^2} + g_0 z_0 = f,$$

$$-a_0 \frac{\partial^2 z_1}{\partial x^2} - b_0 \frac{\partial^2 z_1}{\partial y^2} + g_0 z_1$$

$$= a \frac{\partial^2 z_0}{\partial x^2} + b \frac{\partial^2 z_0}{\partial y^2} + c \frac{\partial z_0}{\partial x} + d \frac{\partial z_0}{\partial y} - g z_0,$$

$$\cdot \quad \cdot \quad \cdot \quad \cdot \quad \cdot \quad \cdot \quad \cdot \quad \cdot \quad \cdot \quad \cdot \quad \cdot \quad \cdot$$

Thus, the method may be used only for those domains D for which the equation with constant coefficients,

$$-a_0 \frac{\partial^2 u}{\partial x^2} - b_0 \frac{\partial^2 u}{\partial y^2} + g_0 u = h(x,y), \qquad u \mid_\Gamma = 0$$

can be solved in an adequate way for any choice of $h(x,y)$. In general, one has to go over to a finite difference equation.

Now, making use of a square mesh and replacing the derivatives in (16) by finite differences, we have

$$\bar{A}u = \left(a_{i,k} + \frac{h}{2} c_{i,k} \right) u_{i+1,k} + \left(a_{i,k} - \frac{h}{2} c_{i,k} \right) u_{i-1,k}$$

$$+ \left(b_{i,k} + \frac{h}{2} d_{i,k} \right) u_{i,k+1} + \left(b_{i,k} - \frac{h}{2} d_{i,k} \right) u_{i,k-1}$$

$$- (2a_{i,k} + 2b_{i,k} + h^2 g_{i,k}) u_{i,k} = h^2 f_{i,k}. \qquad (18)$$

Let $\bar{A}_0$ be the positive definite operator defined by

$$\bar{A}_0 u = (2a_0 + 2b_0 + h^2 g_0) u_{i,k}$$
$$- a_0 (u_{i+1,k} + u_{i-1,k}) - b_0 (u_{i,k+1} + u_{i-1,k}),$$

$$a_0 > 0, \quad b_0 > 0, \quad g_0 \geqq 0.$$

By the use of this, equation (18) can be expressed in a form conducive to the application of an iteration process. We first write

$$\bar{A}u = -\bar{A}_0 u + (\bar{A} + \bar{A}_0) u = h^2 f.$$

The application of $\bar{A}_0^{-1}$ to both sides of this equation then yields

$$u = Tu - h^2 \bar{A}_0^{-1} f, \tag{19}$$

$$T = \bar{A}_0^{-1}(\bar{A} + \bar{A}_0).$$

We now solve (19) by an iteration process. First of all, from the equations

$$(2a_0 + 2b_0 + h^2 g_0)\varepsilon_{i,k}^{(0)} - a_0(\varepsilon_{i+1,k}^{(0)} + \varepsilon_{i-1,k}^{(0)})$$
$$- b_0(\varepsilon_{i,k+1}^{(0)} + \varepsilon_{i,k-1}^{(0)}) = -h^2 f_{i,k}$$

we find $\varepsilon^{(0)} = -h^2 \bar{A}_0^{-1} f$.

We then define

$$u^{(1)} = T\varepsilon^{(0)} - h^2 \bar{A}_0^{-1} f, \quad u^{(1)} = \varepsilon^{(0)} + \varepsilon^{(1)}, \quad \varepsilon^{(1)} = T\varepsilon^{(0)},$$

$$\cdot \quad \cdot \quad \cdot \quad \cdot \quad \cdot \quad \cdot \quad \cdot \quad \cdot \quad \cdot \quad \cdot \quad \cdot \quad \cdot \quad \cdot \quad \cdot \quad \cdot \quad \cdot \quad \cdot \quad \cdot \quad \cdot \quad \cdot$$

$$u^{(n+1)} = Tu^{(n)} - h^2 \bar{A}_0^{-1} f, \quad u^{(n+1)} = u^{(n)} + \varepsilon^{(n)}, \quad \varepsilon^{(n)} = T\varepsilon^{(n-1)},$$

where $\varepsilon^{(n)}$ is determined by

$$\bar{A}_0 \varepsilon^{(n)} = (\bar{A} + \bar{A}_0)\varepsilon^{(n-1)} = \bar{A} u^{(n)} - h^2 f,$$

or explicitly

$$(2a_0 + 2b_0 + h^2 g_0)\varepsilon_{i,k}^{(n)} - a_0(\varepsilon_{i+1,k}^{(n)} + \varepsilon_{i-1,k}^{(n)})$$
$$- b_0(\varepsilon_{i,k+1}^{(n)} + \varepsilon_{i,k-1}^{(n)}) = f_{i,k}^{(n)}, \tag{20}$$

with

$$f_{i,k}^{(n)} = -[2(a_{i,k} - a_0) + 2(b_{i,k} - b_0) + h^2(g_{i,k} - g_0)]\varepsilon_{i,k}^{(n-1)}$$

$$+ \left(a_{i,k} - a_0 + \frac{h}{2}c_{i,k}\right)\varepsilon_{i+1,k}^{(n-1)} + \left(a_{i,k} - a_0 - \frac{h}{2}c_{i,k}\right)\varepsilon_{i-1,k}^{(n-1)}$$

$$+ \left(b_{i,k} - b_0 + \frac{h}{2}d_{i,k}\right)\varepsilon_{i,k+1}^{(n-1)} + \left(b_{i,k} - b_0 - \frac{h}{2}d_{i,k}\right)\varepsilon_{i,k-1}^{(n-1)}$$

$$= \left(a_{i,k} + \frac{h}{2}c_{i,k}\right)u_{i+1,k}^{(n)} + \left(a_{i,k} - \frac{h}{2}c_{i,k}\right)u_{i-1,k}^{(n)}$$

$$+ \left(b_{i,k} + \frac{h}{2}d_{i,k}\right)u_{i,k+1}^{(n)} + \left(b_{i,k} - \frac{h}{2}d_{i,k}\right)u_{i,k-1}^{(n)}$$

$$- [2a_{i,k} + 2b_{i,k} + h^2 g_{i,k}]u_{i,k}^{(n)} - h^2 f_{i,k}.$$

Generally speaking, the sequence $u^{(n)}$ may not converge to the desired solution of (18). Therefore, to obtain the proper solution, one must apply the method of moments. The scalar product to be used in the method is defined just as for the differential operator, namely,

$$[\varepsilon^{(n)}, \varepsilon^{(m)}] = (\bar{A}_0 \varepsilon^{(n)}, \varepsilon^{(m)}) = \sum_{i,k} \varepsilon_{i,k}^{(m)} [(2a_0 + 2b_0 + h^2 g_0) \varepsilon_{i,k}^{(n)}$$
$$- a_0 (\varepsilon_{i+1,k}^{(n)} + \varepsilon_{i,k-1}^{(n)}) - b_0 (\varepsilon_{i,k+1}^{(n)} + \varepsilon_{i,k+1}^{(n)})] = \sum_{i,k} \varepsilon_{i,k}^{(m)} f_{i,k}^{(n)}.$$

It should be noted that the values of $\varepsilon_{i,k}^{(n)}$ at mesh points adjacent to the boundary can be computed using the standard equations (20). These mesh points are distinguished by the fact that the $f_{i,k}$ have a different form on account of $\bar{A}$ being computed from interpolation formulas with unequal spacings.

The constants a_0, b_0, and g_0 are chosen so as to make the approximations converge as fast as possible while at the same time leaving (20) sufficiently simple.

Simplest of all, of course, is to take $a_0 = b_0$ and $g_0 = 0$. The equations (20) then go over into the usual equations for the two-dimensional problem of potential theory which thus permits one to make wide use of an electro-integrator in their solution.

In numerical calculations, a reasonable choice for a_0, b_0, and g_0 would be numbers close to the mean values of the functions a, b, and g in the domain D. Also, if the coefficients a, b, and g vary considerably, then sometimes D can be subdivided and a_0, b_0, and g_0 chosen differently in each subregion. Of course, in this connexion, the definition of scalar product would have to be changed.

Thus, the solution of the finite difference equation with variable coefficients can be reduced to the successive solution of equations with constant coefficients. A way of handling such equations was discussed in §3, Chapter IV.

Let us illustrate the method by considering the axially-symmetric Dirichlet problem. The pertinent equation is

$$\Delta \phi = \frac{\partial^2 \phi}{\partial z^2} + \frac{1}{r} \frac{\partial \phi}{\partial r} + \frac{\partial^2 \phi}{\partial r^2} = 0.$$

The corresponding finite difference equations are given by

$$\left.\begin{array}{r} \left(1 + \dfrac{1}{2k}\right) \phi_{i,k+1} + \phi_{i+1,k} + \left(1 - \dfrac{1}{2k}\right) \phi_{i,k-1} \\ + \phi_{i-1,k} - 4\phi_{i,k} = 0 \quad (k \neq 0), \\ 4\phi_{i,1} + \phi_{i+1,0} + \phi_{i-1,0} - 6\phi_{i,0} = 0 \quad (k = 0), \\ r = kh. \end{array}\right\} \quad (21)$$

At $r = 0$, the Laplace equation becomes

$$\Delta\phi = \frac{\partial^2\phi}{\partial z^2} + 2\frac{\partial^2\phi}{\partial r^2} = 0,$$

We therefore let $a_0 = 1$ and $b_0 = 3/2$, and for the operator $\bar{A}_0$ we take

$$\bar{A}_0\phi = 5\phi_{i,k} - \phi_{i+1,k} - \phi_{i-1,k} - \tfrac{3}{2}(\phi_{i,k+1} + \phi_{i,k-1}).$$

The equations (20) determining the successive corrections assume the form

$$5\varepsilon_{i,k}^{(n)} - \varepsilon_{i+1,k}^{(n)} - \varepsilon_{i-1,k}^{(n)} - \tfrac{3}{2}(\varepsilon_{i,k+1}^{(n)} + \varepsilon_{i,k-1}^{(n)}) = f_{i,k}^{(n)}, \qquad (20')$$

where for $k > 0$

$$f_{i,k}^{(n)} = \left(\frac{1}{2k} - \frac{1}{2}\right)\varepsilon_{i,k+1}^{(n-1)} - \left(\frac{1}{2} + \frac{1}{2k}\right)\varepsilon_{i,k-1}^{(n-1)} + \varepsilon_{i,k}^{(n)}$$

$$= \left(1 + \frac{1}{2k}\right)\phi_{i,k+1}^{(n)} + \phi_{i-1,k}^{(n)} + \left(1 - \frac{1}{2k}\right)\phi_{i,k-1}^{(n)}$$

$$+ \phi_{i+1,k}^{(n)} - h^2 f_{i,k} - 4\phi_{i,k}^{(n)},$$

and

$$f_{i,k}^{(0)} = \varepsilon_{i,1}^{(n-1)} - \varepsilon_{i,0}^{(n-1)} = 4\phi_{i,1}^{(n)} + \phi_{i+1,0}^{(n)} + \phi_{i-1,0}^{(n)} - 6\phi_{i,0}^{(n)} - h^2 f_{i,0}.$$

The successive approximations are then computed iteratively using

$$\phi^{(n)} = \phi^{(0)} + \varepsilon^{(0)} + \varepsilon^{(1)} + \ldots + \varepsilon^{(n)},$$

or by the method of moments for which the scalar product is defined to be

$$[\varepsilon^{(n)}, \varepsilon^{(m)}] = \sum_{i,k} f_{i,k}^{(n)}\varepsilon_{i,k}^{(m)}.$$

After the solution to the finite difference equations (21) has been found, it can be refined by the use of more exact equations. In the present axially-symmetric problem, the following relations hold between the Laplacian and the values of the function at the mesh points:

$$\bar{A}\phi = \left(1 + \frac{1}{2k}\right)\phi_{i,k+1} + \phi_{i+1,k} + \left(1 - \frac{1}{2k}\right)\phi_{i,k-1}$$

$$+ \phi_{i-1,k} - 4\phi_{i,k} = h^2\Delta\phi + O(h^4) \quad (k > 0),$$

$$\bar{A}\phi = 4\phi_{i,1} + \phi_{i+1,0} + \phi_{i-1,0} - 6\phi_{i,0} = h^2\Delta\phi + O(h^4) \quad (k = 0);$$

$$\bar{L}\phi = \left(\frac{2}{3}+\frac{1}{3k}-\frac{1}{12k^2}+\frac{7}{192k^3}\right)\phi_{i,k+1}+\frac{2}{3}(\phi_{i+1,k}+\phi_{i-1,k})$$

$$+\left(\frac{2}{3}-\frac{1}{3k}-\frac{1}{12k^2}-\frac{7}{192k^3}\right)\phi_{i,k-1}$$

$$+\left(\frac{1}{6}+\frac{1}{12k}+\frac{1}{384k^3}\right)(\phi_{i+1,k+1}+\phi_{i-1,k+1})$$

$$+\left(\frac{1}{6}-\frac{1}{12k}-\frac{1}{384k^3}\right)(\phi_{i+1,k-1}+\phi_{i-1,k-1})$$

$$-\left(\frac{10}{3}-\frac{1}{6k^2}\right)\phi_{i,k} = h^2\Delta\phi+\frac{h^4}{12}\Delta\Delta\phi+O(h^6) \quad (k>0),$$

$$\bar{L}\phi = \frac{1}{9}\phi_{i,2}+\frac{20}{9}\phi_{i,1}+\frac{2}{3}(\phi_{i+1,1}+\phi_{i-1,1})$$

$$+\frac{1}{3}(\phi_{i+1,0}+\phi_{i-1,0})-\frac{13}{3}\phi_{i,0} = h^2\Delta\phi+\frac{h^4}{12}\Delta\Delta\phi+O(h^6) \quad (k=0).$$

Thus, $\bar{L}\phi$ may be represented as

$$\bar{L}\phi = \bar{A}\phi+\bar{B}\phi,$$

where $\bar{B}$ is of order h^4.

Let ϕ^* and ϕ^{**} denote the respective solutions of the finite difference equations $\bar{A}\phi^*=0$ and $\bar{L}\phi^{**}=0$.

The function $\eta = \phi^{**}-\phi^*$ then satisfies the equation

$$\bar{L}\eta = -\bar{L}\phi^* \tag{22}$$

or $$\bar{A}\eta+\bar{B}\eta = -\bar{L}\phi^*.$$

Since η is of order h^2, it follows that $\bar{A}\eta = O(h^4)$, $\bar{B}\eta = O(h^6)$ and hence $\bar{L}\phi^*$ is of order h^4. In the replacement of Laplace's equation by the equation $\bar{L}\phi = 0$, terms of order h^6 have been neglected and there is no justification for retaining them either in equation (22). Therefore, the correction may be calculated from the equation

$$\bar{A}\eta = -\bar{L}\phi^* \tag{23}$$

or explicitly

$$\left.\begin{array}{l}\left(1+\frac{1}{2k}\right)\eta_{i,k+1}+\eta_{i+1,k}+\left(1-\frac{1}{2k}\right)\eta_{i,k-1}+\eta_{i-1,k} \\[2mm] \qquad\qquad -4\eta_{i,k} = f_{i,k} \quad (k>0), \\[2mm] 4\eta_{i,1}+\eta_{i+1,0}+\eta_{i-1,0}-6\eta_{i,0} = f_{i,0} \quad (k=0),\end{array}\right\} \tag{23'}$$

with $f_{i,k} = -\bar{L}\phi^*$.

6

A way of solving these equations was described above.

Thus, a boundary value problem for a finite difference equation with variable coefficients may be treated in two ways:

(1) The original finite difference equation is only used to compute the residuals, while the equation corresponding to the two-dimensional problem for Poisson's equation is actually solved by measurements on an electro-integrator. The method of moments is applied to assure the convergence of the approximations and to obtain a solution with a minimum number of iterations.

(2) The equation with variable coefficients is replaced by an equation with constant coefficients having a certain degree of accuracy, as was done in the axially symmetric problem. The equations with variable coefficients are again used just to compute the residuals. After half the unknowns have been eliminated, the equations with constant co-efficients are solved by an iteration process, the method of moments being used to speed up the convergence.

4. Bending of a Beam of Variable Cross-Section

Consider the transverse bending of a beam with a prescribed elastic modulus $EJ(\xi)$ under the action of a longitudinal compression force P and a specific transverse load $p(\xi)$. The coordinate ξ is measured along the beam (Fig. 9). The bending moment satisfies the differential equation

$$\frac{d^2 M}{d\xi^2} + \frac{P}{EJ(\xi)} M = -p(\xi).$$

We treat the case where the elastic modulus is given by

$$EJ(\xi) = \frac{EJ_0}{1 + \left(\frac{\xi}{l}\right)^2},$$

and the compression force $P = EJ_0/l^2$. The transverse load $p(\xi)$ will be assumed to be constant. If the dimensionless variables $x = \xi/l$ and $y = M/l^2 p$ are introduced, the differential equation can be written in the form

$$-y'' - (1 + x^2) y = 1. \tag{24}$$

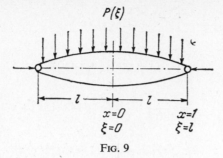

$$P(\xi)$$

$$x=0 \qquad x=1$$
$$\xi=0 \qquad \xi=l$$

FIG. 9

The prime denotes differentiation with respect to x. For a beam pinned at its supports ($M = 0$ there), the boundary conditions are

$$y(-1) = y(1) = 0. \tag{25}$$

In this example, the operators introduced in §2 assume the form (except for a sign)

$$Ay = -y'' - (1+x^2)y,$$

$$A_0 y = -y'', \quad Ky = (1+x^2)y.$$

The sequence of functions $z_k(x)$ is determined recursively from the equations

$$-z_k''(x) = (1+x^2)z_{k-1}(x),$$

$$-z_0''(x) = 1, \quad z_k(-1) = z_k(1) = 0.$$

Solving the first few of them, we obtain

$$z_0(x) = \tfrac{1}{2}(1-x^2),$$

$$z_1(x) = \tfrac{1}{60}(14 - 15x^2 + x^6).$$

The appropriate scalar products are then given by

$$[z_0, z_0] = (A_0 z_0, z_0) = -\int_{-1}^{1} z_0''(x)z_0(x)\, dx$$

$$= \int_{-1}^{1} \tfrac{1}{2}(1-x^2)\, dx = 0.666667,$$

$$[z_1, z_0] = -\int_{-1}^{1} z_1''(x)z_0(x)\, dx = \int_{-1}^{1} (1+x^2)z_0^2(x)\, dx$$

$$= \tfrac{1}{2}\int_{-1}^{1} (1-x^4)(1-x^2)\, dx = 0.304762,$$

$$[z_1, z_1] = [z_2, z_0] = -\int_{-1}^{1} z_2''(x) z_0(x) \, dx$$

$$= \int_{-1}^{1} (1+x^2) z_1(x) z_0(x) \, dx$$

$$= \frac{1}{120} \int_{-1}^{1} (1-x^4)(14-15x^2+x^6) \, dx = 0.139913,$$

$$[z_2, z_1] = -\int_{-1}^{1} z_2''(x) z_1(x) \, dx = \int_{-1}^{1} (1+x^2) z_1^2(x) \, dx$$

$$= \frac{1}{360} \int_{-1}^{1} (1+x^2)(14-15x^2+x^6)^2 \, dx = 10^{-2} \cdot 6.42613.$$

If we write the equation (24) in the form

$$y = Ty + z_0$$

with $T = A_0^{-1} K$, we can find its approximate solution on the basis of formula (4). The results for $n=1$ and $n=2$ are given below.

For $n=1$, $y_1(x) = a_0 z_0(x)$,

$$a_0 = 1 - \frac{\alpha_0}{P_1(1)} = 1 - \frac{\alpha_0}{1+\alpha_0} = \frac{1}{1+\alpha_0}, \quad P_1(\lambda) = \lambda + \alpha_0,$$

the coefficient α_0 being obtained from

$$[z_0, z_0]\alpha_0 + [z_1, z_0] = 0.666667\alpha_0 + 0.304762 = 0.$$

Solving for α_0, we conclude that

$$\alpha_0 = -0.457143,$$

$$a_0 = 1.84211,$$

$$y_1(x) = 0.92106(1-x^2).$$

The second approximation ($n=2$) is given by

$$y_2(x) = a_0 z_0(x) + a_1 z_1(x),$$

with

$$a_0 = 1 - \frac{\alpha_0}{P_2(1)} = 1 - \frac{\alpha_0}{1+\alpha_1+\alpha_0} = \frac{1+\alpha_1}{1+\alpha_1+\alpha_0},$$

$$a_1 = a_0 - \frac{\alpha_1}{P_2(1)} = \frac{1}{1+\alpha_1+\alpha_0}.$$

The coefficients α_0 and α_1 satisfy the equations

$$\left.\begin{array}{l} [z_0, z_0]\alpha_0 + [z_1, z_0]\alpha_1 + [z_2, z_0] = 0, \\ [z_1, z_0]\alpha_0 + [z_1, z_1]\alpha_1 + [z_2, z_1] = 0, \end{array}\right\}$$

$$\left.\begin{array}{l} 0.666667\alpha_0 + 0.304762\alpha_1 + 0.139913 = 0, \\ 0.304762\alpha_0 + 0.139913\alpha_1 + 0.0642613 = 0. \end{array}\right\}$$

The solution of this system then leads to the results

$$\alpha_0 = 10^{-2} \cdot 2.1781,$$

$$\alpha_1 = -0.50674,$$

$$a_0 = 0.95771,$$

$$a_1 = 1.9416,$$

$$y_2(x) = 0.477885(1-x^2) + 0.032360(14 - 15x^2 + x^6).$$

For comparison sake, we have tabulated some values of the two approximate solutions and of the highly accurate solution obtained by means of numerical integration.

x	$y_1(x)$	$y_2(x)$	$y(x)$
0	0.92106	0.93189	0.93209
0.2	0.88422	0.89332	0.89345
0.4	0.77369	0.77774	0.77772
0.6	0.58948	0.58617	0.58616
0.8	0.33158	0.32325	0.32325
1	0	0	0

5. The Field of an Electrostatic Electron Lens

As a final application, we give the calculation of the electrostatic field of an electron lens made up of two bounded conducting circular cylinders (Fig. 10).

In cylindrical coordinates, the electrostatic potential in the space between the electrodes satisfies Laplace's equation

$$\Delta\phi = \frac{\partial^2\phi}{\partial z^2} + \frac{1}{r}\frac{\partial\phi}{\partial r} + \frac{\partial^2\phi}{\partial r^2} = 0.$$

On the outer cylinder, $\phi = 0$, and on the inner one, $\phi = 1$. The initial approximation ϕ^* to the solution of the finite difference equations (21) was obtained by means of an electro-integrator (Fig. 11, the lower numbers).

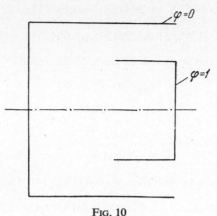

$\varphi = 0$

$\varphi = 1$

FIG. 10

By the use of the more exact formulas, the residuals $f_{i,k} = -\bar{L}\phi^*$ can then be written out:

$$f_{i,k} = \left(\frac{10}{3} - \frac{1}{6k^2}\right)\phi^*_{i,k} - \left(\frac{2}{3} + \frac{1}{3k} - \frac{1}{12k^2} + \frac{7}{192k^3}\right)\phi^*_{i,k+1}$$

$$- \frac{2}{3}(\phi^*_{i+1,k} + \phi^*_{i-1,k}) - \left(\frac{2}{3} - \frac{1}{3k} - \frac{1}{12k^2} - \frac{7}{192k^3}\right)\phi^*_{i,k-1}$$

$$- \left(\frac{1}{6} + \frac{1}{12k} + \frac{1}{384k^3}\right)(\phi^*_{i+1,k+1} + \phi^*_{i-1,k+1})$$

$$- \left(\frac{1}{6} - \frac{1}{12k} - \frac{1}{384k^3}\right)(\phi^*_{i+1,k-1} + \phi^*_{i-1,k-1}) \quad (k > 0),$$

$$f_{i,0} = \frac{13}{3}\phi^*_{i,0} - \frac{1}{9}\phi^*_{i,2} - \frac{20}{9}\phi^*_{i,1} - \frac{2}{3}(\phi^*_{i+1,1} + \phi^*_{i-1,1})$$

$$- \frac{1}{3}(\phi^*_{i+1,0} + \phi^*_{i-1,0}) \quad (k = 0).$$

The values of $f_{i,k}$ have also been tabulated in Fig. 11 (the upper numbers).

$$\varphi^*$$

12 / 15	-14 / 33	13 / 54	2 / 83	22 / 122	40 / 173	-84 / 228	21 / 256	-14 / 271	-10 / 281	-43 / 297
7 / 31	-18 / 67	-20 / 111	-9 / 170	22 / 254	202 / 374	-340 / 525	53 / 576	21 / 595	-2 / 607	-41 / 625
-4 / 46	-18 / 98	-33 / 162	-51 / 248	-150 / 375	-564 / 584					
-5 / 58	-39 / 123	-11 / 200	1 / 300	46 / 435	266 / 618	-450 / 839	105 / 924	34 / 962	17 / 981	8 / 992
7 / 66	2 / 139	-3 / 225	3 / 331	5 / 463	70 / 618	-132 / 776	-5 / 875	3 / 932	-9 / 965	2 / 985
4 / 71	-1 / 149	-2 / 239	-8 / 347	13 / 474	-1 / 615	-65 / 750	-19 / 849	15 / 913	32 / 953	1 / 980
-12 / 73	2 / 152	-26 / 244	-14 / 352	-36 / 478	17 / 613	-21 / 742	22 / 840	1 / 907	-13 / 950	12 / 978

(Row labels at left, top to bottom: 6, 5, 4, 3, 2, 1, 0)

FIG. 11

To compute η, the error in the approximate solution ϕ^*, we solve the equations (23) by successive approximations, the first approximation $\eta^{(0)}$ being obtained from (20'):

$$5\eta_{i,k}^{(0)} - \eta_{i+1,k}^{(0)} - \eta_{i-1,k}^{(0)} - \tfrac{3}{2}(\eta_{i,k+1}^{(0)} + \eta_{i,k-1}^{(0)}) = f_{i,k}^{(0)}.$$

Before solving these equations, we eliminate half the unknowns. The equations relating the unknowns at the mesh points indicated by the dots in Fig. 11 have the following forms.

(a) At interior mesh points:

$$\eta_{i,k}^{(0)} = \tfrac{1}{74}\left[12(\eta_{i+1,k+1}^{(0)} + \eta_{i-1,k+1}^{(0)} + \eta_{i+1,k-1}^{(0)} + \eta_{i-1,k-1}^{(0)})\right.$$
$$+ 4(\eta_{i+2,k}^{(0)} + \eta_{i-2,k}^{(0)}) + 9(\eta_{i,k+2}^{(0)} + \eta_{i,k-2}^{(0)})\right] + \tfrac{1}{37}\left[10f_{i,k}\right.$$
$$\left. + 2(f_{i+1,k} + f_{i-1,k}) + 3(f_{i,k+1} + f_{i,k-1})\right].$$

(b) At mesh points adjacent to the ends of the cylinders:

$$(\eta_{i-1,k}^{(0)} = \eta_{i-1,k+1}^{(0)} = \eta_{i-1,k-1}^{(0)} = 0)$$
$$\eta_{i,k}^{(0)} = \tfrac{1}{78}\left[12(\eta_{i+1,k+1}^{(0)} + \eta_{i+1,k-1}^{(0)}) + 4\eta_{i+2,k}^{(0)} + 9(\eta_{i,k+2}^{(0)}\right.$$
$$\left. + \eta_{i,k-2}^{(0)})\right] + \tfrac{1}{39}\left[10f_{i,k} + 2f_{i+1,k} + 3(f_{i,k+1} + f_{i,k-1})\right].$$

Similar formulas hold at those mesh points where

$$\eta_{i+1,k}^{(0)} = \eta_{i+1,k+1}^{(0)} = \eta_{i+1,k-1}^{(0)} = 0.$$

(c) At mesh points adjacent to the sides of the cylinders where
$\eta^{(0)}_{i,k+1} = \eta^{(0)}_{i-1,k+1} = \eta^{(0)}_{i+1,k+1} = 0$:

$$\eta^{(0)}_{i,k} = \tfrac{1}{83}\left[12(\eta^{(0)}_{i+1,k-1}+\eta^{(0)}_{i-1,k-1})+4(\eta^{(0)}_{i+2,k}+\eta^{(0)}_{i-2,k})\right.$$
$$\left.+9\eta^{(0)}_{i,k-2}\right]+\tfrac{1}{83}\left[20f_{i,k}+4(f_{i+1,k}+f_{i-1,k})+6f_{i,k-1}\right].$$

(d) At mesh points adjacent to the corners where

$$\eta^{(0)}_{i-1,k} = \eta^{(0)}_{i-1,k-1} = \eta^{(0)}_{i-1,k+1} = \eta^{(0)}_{i,k+1} = \eta^{(0)}_{i+1,k+1} = 0,$$

we have

$$\eta^{(0)}_{i,k} = \tfrac{1}{87}\left[12\eta^{(0)}_{i+1,k-1}+4\eta^{(0)}_{i+2,k}+9\eta^{(0)}_{i,k-2}\right]+\tfrac{1}{87}\left[20f_{i,k}\right.$$
$$\left.+4f_{i+1,k}-6f_{i,k-1}\right].$$

The free terms have been tabulated for the above formulas in Fig. 12 (the numbers below the dashes). Choosing them to be an initial approximation, we then compute successive corrections by Seidel's method according to rows starting with the upper left-hand corner.

```
 -1        -3        -3        -1              0                0
 -1        -3        -4        -1              0                0
 -1        -5        -6        -4             -2               -1
 -1  -3   -3  -5  -11  -4   -1    0   -3    0    0
  3  -4    1  -7    9  -5  -42    0   -1    0  -13
  •  -5    •  -8    •  -7    •   -1    •    0    •
 -2  -5   -5 -15   -6 -18        -8        -3
 -3  -8   -? -6    -8  -5        -1        -2
 -3        •  -9    • -13        •
 -4  -4  -12  -7   -6  -6        -3        -1
 -2  -5  -15  -9  -68  -9        -5        -1
  •  -7       -12   • -11        -4         0
 -3  -7   -7 -18   -9 -25   -7  -11  -4    1  -1
 -3 -13   -8  -2  -11  10  -10    5  -5    5  -1
 -3        •  -9    • -12  -13        -5    •    1
 -4  -5  -11  -9  -20  -6   -6   -6  -5  -3    2
  2  -6   -2 -10   10 -12  -74   -9   4  -3    1
  •  -6       •    -11  • -17    •  -13    •  -2    •
 -3  -7   -7  -9   -9 -20   -7  -17  -4    2  -1
 -3   0   -8  -2  -11   4  -10   -6  -6    8  -1
 -3        •  -9    • -14    • -14        -7    •   -1
 -3       -10      -13            -33        -7        4
 -2       -8       -7             -14         3        3
  •        •        •             •          •        •
```

FIG. 12

Fig. 12 gives the results of four iterations, which we denote respectively by $\varepsilon^{(0)}$, $\varepsilon^{(1)}$, $\varepsilon^{(2)}$, $\varepsilon^{(3)}$. To speed up the convergence of the iterations, we apply the method of moments, taking the scalar product

FIG. 13

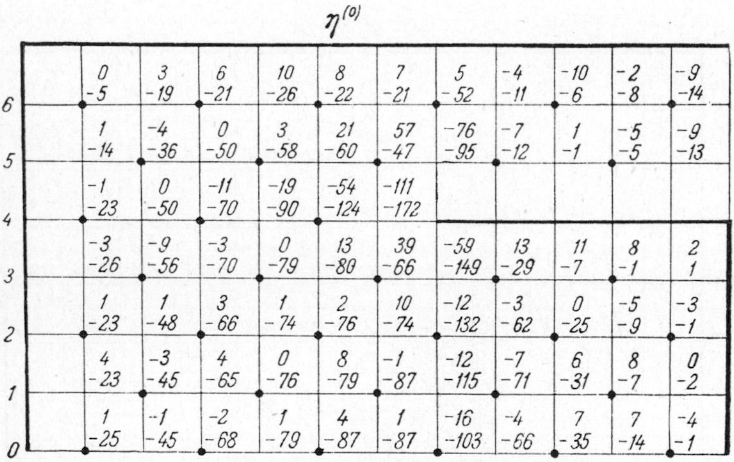

$\eta^{(0)}$

0 / -5	3 / -19	6 / -21	10 / -26	8 / -22	7 / -21	5 / -52	-4 / -11	-10 / -6	-2 / -8	-9 / -14
1 / -14	-4 / -36	0 / -50	3 / -58	21 / -60	57 / -47	-76 / -95	-7 / -12	1 / -1	-5 / -5	-9 / -13
-1 / -23	0 / -50	-11 / -70	-19 / -90	-54 / -124	-111 / -172					
-3 / -26	-9 / -56	-3 / -70	0 / -79	13 / -80	39 / -66	-59 / -149	13 / -29	11 / -7	8 / -1	2 / 1
1 / -23	1 / -48	3 / -66	1 / -74	2 / -76	10 / -74	-12 / -132	-3 / -62	0 / -25	-5 / -9	-3 / -1
4 / -23	-3 / -45	4 / -65	0 / -76	8 / -79	-1 / -87	-12 / -115	-7 / -71	6 / -31	8 / -7	0 / -2
1 / -25	-1 / -45	-2 / -68	1 / -79	4 / -87	1 / -87	-16 / -103	-4 / -66	7 / -35	7 / -14	-4 / -1

Row labels (left, top to bottom): 6, 5, 4, 3, 2, 1, 0

FIG. 14

$$\eta^{(1)}$$

6	-1 / -5	0 / -19	-1 / -20	5 / -25	-2 / -20	2 / -21	4 / -57	-2 / -15	-3 / -10	-3 / -10	0 / -17
5	4 / -15	4 / -40	1 / -54	1 / -62	9 / -63	17 / -49	-18 / -113	-8 / -18	1 / -4	-5 / -7	-3 / -16
4	3 / -26	-6 / -54	-4 / -79	-8 / -104	-18 / -147	-25 / -202					
3	1 / -30	-5 / -62	1 / -78	-3 / -88	4 / -90	0 / -74	-7 / -168	2 / -32	1 / -5	3 / 1	0 / 2
2	3 / -26	0 / -52	-3 / -70	1 / -80	-4 / -82	4 / -82	0 / -143	0 / -70	-1 / -26	-5 / -8	0 / -1
1	2 / -25	-1 / -49	-4 / -68	0 / -80	0 / -83	-2 / -96	0 / -131	-1 / -81	2 / -32	-6 / -3	0 / -1
0	7 / -28	1 / -49	-4 / -71	1 / -83	5 / -92	-2 / -96	-3 / -119	-1 / -76	2 / -36	5 / -11	3 / -1

Fig. 15

$$\varphi^{**}$$

6	145	311	520	806	1201	1710	2223	2545	2699	2800	2953
5	296	631	1056	1638	2479	3692	5133	5740	5946	6062	6233
4	434	925	1540	2373	3598	5632					
3	550	1167	1921	2910	4260	6104	8220	9208	9615	9812	9922
2	635	1338	2179	3230	4547	6098	7612	8680	9294	9641	9849
1	685	1441	2321	3390	4657	6054	7369	8409	9098	9526	9799
0	703	1471	2368	3437	4689	6034	7301	8324	9034	9490	9780

Fig. 16

to be the sum of products of the values of the functions at the mesh points:

$$(\varepsilon^{(1)}, \varepsilon^{(1)}) = 2391, \quad (\varepsilon^{(1)}, \varepsilon^{(2)}) = 1851, \quad (\varepsilon^{(1)}, \varepsilon^{(3)}) = 1421,$$

$$(\varepsilon^{(2)}, \varepsilon^{(2)}) = 1473, \quad (\varepsilon^{(2)}, \varepsilon^{(3)}) = 1137,$$

$$2391\alpha_0 + 1891\alpha_1 + 1421 = 0, \quad \alpha_0 = +0.124,$$

$$1851\alpha_0 + 1421\alpha_1 + 1137 = 0, \quad \alpha_1 = -0.927,$$

$$\eta^{(0)} \approx \varepsilon^{(0)} + 0.36\varepsilon^{(1)} + 5\varepsilon^{(2)}.$$

The resulting approximate solution (the lower numbers in Fig. 13) is again refined by the Seidel method.

Thus, the computation of $\eta^{(0)}$ (Fig. 14) requires 8 iterations and one step in the method of moments for $n = 2$. A repetition of the procedure yields the next approximation for η (Fig. 15). The final solution ϕ^{**} is given in Fig. 16.

Bibliography

(Starred items are in Russian)

ABRAMOV, A. A.
*(1) A method of speeding up the convergence of iterative processes. *Doklady Akad. nauk* 74, 6 (1950), 1051–2.
BANACH, S.
(1) *Théorie des opérations linéaires*. Warsaw, 1932.
BIRMAN, M. SH.
*(1) Some estimates for the method of steepest descent. *Uspekhi matem. nauk.*, V, No. 3 (1950), 152–5.
*(2) Calculation of eigenvalues by the method of steepest descent. *Zap. Leningrad gorn. in-ta*, Vol. XXVII, No. 1 (1952), 209–15.
CHEBYSHEV, P. L.
(1) Collected works. Chelsea Publishing Company, 1962.
GAVURIN, M. K.
*(1) Application of best approximating polynomials to improving the convergence of iterative processes. *Uspekhi matem. nauk*, V, No. 3 (1950), 156–60.
GERONIMUS, YA. L.
(1) *Theory of Orthogonal Polynomials*. Gostekhizdat, 1950.
HESTENES, M. and KARUSH, W.
(1) Method of gradients for the calculation of the characteristic roots and vectors of a real symmetric matrix. *J. Res. Nat. Bur. Standards*, Vol. 47, No. 1 (1951), 45–61.
HESTENES, M. and STIEFEL, E.
(1) Method of conjugate gradients for solving linear systems. *J. Res. Nat. Bur. Standards*, Vol. 49, No. 6 (1952), 409–36.
IOFFE, G. SH.
*(1) *Influence of a Sperry-type automatic pilot on the lateral stability of an airplane*. Izdanie BNT, 1946.
KANTOROVICH, L. V.
*(1) An effective method of solving extremal problems for quadratic functionals. *Doklady Akad. Nauk* 48, 7 (1945), 483–7.
*(2) On the method of steepest descent. *Doklay Akad. Nauk* 56, 3 (1947), 233–6.
*(3) Functional analysis and applied mathematics. *Uspekhi matem. nauk*, III, No. 6 (1948), 89–184.
KARUSH, W.
(1) Convergence of a method of solving linear problems. *Proc. Amer. Math. Soc.* 3 (1952), 839–51.
KELDYSH, M. V.
*(1) On Galerkin's method for solving boundary value problems. *Izv. Akad. Nauk SSSR, ser. matem.* 6 (1942), 309–30.
KELLOGG, O.
(1) On the existence and closure of sets of characteristic functions. *Math. Ann.*, Vol. 86 (1922), 14–17.

KRASNOSELSKY, M. A.
*(1) Some methods of computing approximately the eigenvalues and eigenvectors of a positive definite matrix. *Uspekhi matem. nauk*, XI, No. 3 (1956), 151–8.
*(2) *Topological Methods in the Theory of Non-Linear Integral Equations.* Gostekhizdat, Moscow, 1956.
KRYLOV, A. N.
*(1) On the numerical solution of equations, which determine the oscillation frequencies of physical systems in engineering problems. *Izv. Akad. Nauk SSSR, ser. fiz-matem.* (1931), 491–539.
*(2) On some differential equations of mathematical physics. *Akad. Nauk SSSR* (1933).
LANCZOS, C.
(1) An iteration method for the solution of the eigenvalue problem of linear differential and integral operators. *J. Res. Nat. Bur. of Standards*, Vol. 45, No. 4 (1950), 255–80.
(2) Solution of systems of linear equations by minimized iterations. *J. Res. Nat. Bur. Standards*, Vol. 49, No. 1 (1952), 33–53.
LIOUVILLE, J.
(1) Sur le développement des fonctions ou parties des fonctions en séries dont les divers termes sont assujetis à satisfaire à une même équation différentielle du second ordre, contenant un paramètre variable. *Journal de math. pur. et appl.*, I (1836), 253–65; II (1837), 16–35, 418–36.
LYUSTERNIK, L. A.
*(1) Remarks on the numerical solution of boundary value problems for Laplace's equation and the computation of eigenvalues by a difference method. *Trudy Matem. In-ta Akad. Nauk SSSR*, XX (1947), 49–64.
*(2) Solution of linear algebraic problems by the method of continued fractions. *Transactions of a seminar on functional analysis*, No. 2, Voronezh (1956), 85–90.
*(3) Difference approximations of the Laplacian operator. *Uspekhi matem. nauk*, IX, No. 2 (1954), 3–66.
MARKOV, A. A.
*(1) *Selected works on the theory of continued fractions and the theory of functions least deviating from zero.* Gostekhizdat, Moscow-Leningrad, 1948.
MIKHLIN, S. G.
*(1) *Direct Methods in Mathematical Physics.* Gostekhizdat, Moscow, 1950.
(2) *Integral Equations.* Pergamon Press (1955).
MILNE, W.
(1) *Numerical Solution of Differential Equations*, John Wiley and Sons, New New York, 1953.
MISES, R. VON and POLLACZEK-GEIRINGER, H.
(1) Praktische Verfahren der Gleichungsauflösung. *Z. für Math. und Mech.*, 9 (1929), 58–77.
NEUMANN, C.
(1) *Untersuchungen über das logarithmische und Newtonische Potential.* Leipzig, 1877.
POLSKY, N.
*(1) Some generalizations of Galerkin's method. *Doklady Akad. Nauk*, Vol. 86, No. 3 (1952), 469–72.
RELLICH, F.
(1) Störungstheorie der Spectrazerlegung. I, II, III, IV, V. *Math. Ann.*, 113 (1936), 600–19; 113 (1936), 667–85; 116 (1939), 555–70; 117 (1940), 356–82; 118 (1942), 462–84.

SCARBOROUGH, J. R.
(1) *Numerical Mathematical Analysis*, 5th ed. Johns Hopkins Press, Baltimore, 1962.
SCHMIDT, E.
(1) Auflösung der allgemeiner linearen Integralgleichung. *Math. Ann.*, **64** (1907), 161–74.
SHOHAT, M.
(1) Théorie générale des polynomes ortogonaux de Tschebyscheff. *Mémorial des sciences Math. fasc.* LXVI (1934).
SHORTLEY, G.
(1) Use of Tschebyscheff polynomials in boundary value problems. *J. of Appl. Phys.*, Vol. **24**, No. 4 (1953), 392–396.
SOLODOVNIKOV, V. V.
*(1) *The Frequency Method of Constructing Transients*. Gostekhizdat, Moscow, 1955.
STESIN, I. M.
*(1) Calculation of eigenvalues with the help of continued fractions. *Uspekhi matem. nauk*, IX, No. 2 (60), (1954), 191–8.
STIELTJES, T.
(1) *Investigation of Continued Fractions*. Ann. de la Fac. Sci. Toulouse, Paris, vol. 8–9, 1894–1895.
TEMPLE, G.
(1) The general theory of relaxation methods applied to linear systems. *Proc. Royal Soc. of Lond.* (A), Vol. **169** (1939), 476–500.
VOROBYEV, YU. V.
*(1) Orthogonal operator polynomials and approximate methods of determining the spectrum of a bounded linear operator. *Uspekhi mathem. nauk*, IX, No. 2 (1954), 191–8.
*(2) Application of orthogonal operator polynomials in the solution of non-homogeneous linear equations. *Uspekhi matem. nauk*, X, No. 1 (1955), 89–96.
*(3) Method of moments for non-self-adjoint linear operators and speeding up the convergence of iterative processes. *Uspekhi matem. nauk*, XI, No. 2 (1956), 161–7.
*(4) Method of moments in oscillation problems for linear systems. Computational Mathematics (*Computational center Akad Nauk SSSR*), sb. 1 (1957), 23–33.

Index